to Grandma
with love from Kathryn
                              x x
         Christmas
              1991

GRANDMOTHERS

GRANDMOTHERS

talking

to

NELL DUNN

Chatto & Windus
LONDON

Published in 1991 by
Chatto & Windus Ltd
20 Vauxhall Bridge Road
London SW1V 2SA

A CIP catalogue record for this book is
available from the British Library.

ISBN 0 7011 3578 6

Printed and bound in Great Britain by
Mackays of Chatham plc, Chatham, Kent

CONTENTS

*To the grandmothers in this book, with warm
thanks for their unstinting help and to all their
grandchildren. Also to my mother, for being a
grandmother to my sons.*

ACKNOWLEDGEMENTS

*With grateful thanks to my publishers:
Carmen Callil, who rescued this book, and
Jonathan Burnham, who edited it.*

Introduction

. . . according to the best of my remembrance, my grandmother was the wickedest and the worst old woman that ever lived. If I got a little pair of shoes by any chance, she would take 'em off and sell 'em for a drink. Why I have known that grandmother of mine lie in her bed and drink fourteen glasses of liquor before breakfast!

From *Hard Times*   Charles Dickens

ONE SUMMER DAY, as I was passing in the street, I saw a woman in her sixties carrying a bunch of flowers freshly picked from a garden. She was ringing a doorbell, and seconds later the door opened and a child jumped into her arms. A young woman appeared; she took the flowers, they spoke and kissed and went inside. Something to do with the welcome and the bringing of the flowers intrigued and touched me. I guessed she was a grandmother.

Later the same year I met a woman in Richmond Park where I was walking with Ivy and May, my Jack Russells. She told me she had moved to London to be near her daughter whose husband had died suddenly leaving her alone with a little girl. She looked after the child during the day whilst her daughter went out to work. In the evening she went back to her own flat, a short bus-ride away. She herself was also newly widowed and a countrywoman, and I wondered if this relationship with her little granddaughter was a god-send or a burden. I became intrigued by the grand-child/grandmother relationship and decided to write a book about it.

A week or two later I learnt that I was to become a grandmother. Now I saw the purpose of the book: I needed help. Women run a marvellous kind of Mafia where information circulates instead of heroin or gold. I wanted to tap in on the Grandmothers' Mafia! I asked the ones I knew if they would talk to me about their memories of their own grandmothers and what it was like to have grandchildren. My friends' friends also came forward, though Jackie is the only woman I didn't know at all. In a series of conversations, sometimes just one long afternoon drifting through to evening and opening a bottle of wine and talking of other things, we explored the terrain. In some of these women's lives grandmothers had been overwhelmingly important, and I realised what a strong and vivid extension of a child's world a grandmother can be and vice versa.

So this is a book about fourteen women remembering our own grandmothers and talking about our grandchildren.

CHAPTER I

Nell

MY GRANDMOTHER

EVER SINCE I first remember seeing my maternal grandmother I knew I was like her: that narrow face, those worried
eyes. When I was about seven she asked me who was the
most important person in the world to be friends with. She
eventually told me the answer was 'Yourself'. I loved being
with her and with my mother and my sister, all of us
together, this woman's world. Her name was Vera.

Once she took me to visit a cousin of hers who lay on a
sofa in a grand house: 'I never sit, I always lie; it preserves
a woman's beauty.' Ever since then I too have never sat, but
always lain. My grandmother wore soft tweed suits with
capes to match and embroidered satin nightdresses. I learnt
later that they were hand-me-downs from the cousin who
always lay. When I was quite a little girl, she told me to
pinch the bridge of my nose every morning when I woke
up so I would have an elegant narrow nose and not a boxer's
snout. She also told me not to frown as this would make
'cross' lines on my face.

When I went to stay with my grandmother, I slept with
her in the double bed with the giant coronet embroidered
on the white satin bedhead. We lay side by side under the
white satin coverlet which also had a coronet to match. If I

moved I woke her up, so I had to lie very still, and I longed for her to go to sleep so I could wriggle. It was on one of these visits that she told me her own mother had died when she was ten. She only heard about her death when her nanny came in in the morning and said, 'Which dress will you wear today, Miss Vera?'

'My cherry dress please, Nanny.'

'You can't wear your cherry dress today, Miss Vera, because your mother died in the night.'

During the First World War she had driven an ambulance and been very dashing, so history relates. In the Second World War she worked for the Red Cross packing cardboard boxes with food for prisoners of war. My mother took me and my sister to see her at work, and she paused for a while to show us the little bars of chocolate and the packets of ten cigarettes that went into each small cardboard box. She let us help pack them. She was already a widow, but she seemed happy in a room full of other busily occupied women. Later, after the war, she appeared pale and lost, and it seems sad that this generation of ladylike women were excluded from everyday employment and forced by their ladylike ways into the servitude of boredom.

Much later, when she was in a convent that looked after elderly people, I used to take my own children to see 'Great-Gran' as she was called. We'd go out into the overgrown garden and sit on a bench while she fed the cats with morsels she had saved from her breakfast and told us stories about her Alsatian who had once followed a train she was travelling on, running along the tracks for nearly a hundred miles and meeting her at the other end. She told us about going to stay with her army brother in India, and riding side-saddle and hunting in Ireland, and once of having to work her passage home on an ocean liner to raise money in England because my grandfather had lost everything on the gambling tables and was being kept a prisoner at the Grand Hotel in

Casablanca till he had paid the bill. I never knew if it was the Irish blood that invented these stories. Once when she was very, very old we took her for a walk and she fell in a stream. Her great-grandsons tried to pull her out, but she got the giggles and much to their glee flopped back in the muddy water.

Although I loved her and knew that in her own way and of her own time, she had been a good grandmother, I didn't want to be the same kind of grandmother. I wanted to know my grandson better from the beginning. I wanted us to be ordinary and everyday with each other. I wanted to be able to be cross with him and for him to be cross with me. I remember in Márquez' novel, *Love in the Time of Cholera* somebody says, ' "By raising my children I got to know them and they got to know me and we became friends" '. In a milder sense this is what I hope for: that by helping to take care of my own little grandson, Cato, we shall become friends.

My grandson, Cato, and his family

Roc, the eldest of my three sons, is Cato's father. Cassia is his mother; Nina is Cassia's mother and my co-grandmother. A home birth in Clerkenwell Green had been planned, but after Cassia had been eighteen hours in labour with Roc beside her and an excellent midwife attending, and Nina and I in the kitchen making food and drinks for everyone in a heat wave, it was decided that she was in too much pain and the baby wasn't making good progress. She was carried down the five flights of stairs into an ambulance and taken to hospital, with Nina and I following in the midwife's car.

Cassia and Cato came home after only six hours in hospital, and Nina and I took it in turns for those first few days to shop and cook in the high-up Clerkenwell flat. 'Don't expect any feelings, don't expect to be happy, just get on with being useful,' I told myself, yet I felt quite lost. I wasn't the mother of the child. There was my eldest son with his eldest son, with new calls on his affection and new responsibilities. I thought, 'Who does he think he is, this little intruder?' I had to get used to being a grandmother and not the little princess in the bed with the little prince – as I had been when his father was born. Instead, there I was with sleeves rolled up, being useful.

I felt big and clumsy beside this tiny creature who trusted me not to drown him, who half-opened his little shut eyes and uncomplainingly blinked at me, the clumsy grand-mother in the apron, dredging up lost memories of how to hold him safely in the plastic bowl, my elbow crooked under his small skinny back, remembering to test the water with the inside of my wrist so it wouldn't be too hot on his new-laid skin. All that tenderness, and yet I was adrift, speechless, uneasy with myself and my new title, 'grandmother'. As a mother I had been so in charge of my children; they were my little brood. We were here, we were there, and I became strong through bringing them up. They were very loyal and we were all together. What I found hard in becoming a grandmother was that I was much lower down the power scale. It was a humbling experience.

I knew I had to make my own relationship with Cato with no one else there. It was a private matter between me and him. I didn't expect this birth to be such an enormous event in my life. Here I was faced with a little baby, who wasn't mine, and I saw I had to make a move to love without yet being loved. I came up against this icy, tight and calculating part of me: 'Why should I give him anything? He's not mine.' I did all the right things in the practical sense, but the love was slow in coming. Very slow.

Then one afternoon I'd taken him for a walk in the park nearby. He was about three months old and his mother was still breastfeeding him, so I couldn't go far. I was sitting on a bench in the rose garden when two Indian women came up with a little girl. They started admiring him and asked if they could hold him. It turned out they were mother, daughter and granddaughter, and they were full of pleasure as they sat beside me on the bench, the sun glinting on their sparkling saris, and congratulated me on my immense good fortune at having a beautiful grandson. I felt very proud and then, as they handed him back, he smiled at me and I was suddenly, all at once, bowled over. Overcome, I hid my face in his warm little stomach and I knew that, yes, I was immensely fortunate! And so it had begun, me and my friend Cato.

During that autumn we got to know each other on our little adventures around his neighbourhood. One afternoon at dusk we watched while a man with a van full of dresses on railings screamed at an Asian woman in the doorway of a house. She was obviously an outworker who had not completed her garment quota. Suddenly she turned on him and flung a pile of clothes out of her door on to the wet pavement and screamed back at him in a language I couldn't understand. Another afternoon we caught a runaway puppy which was heading helter-skelter for the road down a little path. I managed to block its way with the pushchair and it nearly hurtled into Cato's lap. We caught it and gave it to its tearful owner.

Then at last he was weaned and able to come to my house for a day every other week. I fetched him at about ten and we'd transfer the car seat to my car and sometimes we'd go straight to Richmond Park with Ivy and May. In the cold weather I'd bundle him up in a blanket and push the pushchair fast to keep warm. When the sun shone I'd sit him on the short turf beside me and we'd watch Ivy and May disappear down rabbit-holes and swim in the ponds.

Ivy was always pleased to see Cato. From the very first time he came over she recognised him as a member of her family and could hardly be prevented from boisterously licking his face. May was more circumspect. Once when she was sitting beside me on the sofa, Cato was on my knee and stretched out a hand towards her. She growled at him and, without thinking, I hit her hard. I had never hit her before and she raced from the room mortified. Now when he's there she prefers to sit in another room. I feel a bit sad about this as I like her with me and I want them all to be friends. Perhaps they will be eventually, but till then Cato comes first. When he goes home I spend time making a fuss of Ivy and May. We sit together on the sofa and get back in touch.

When Cassia suggested I take Cato down to the cottage for a night I thought, 'He'll be in a strange house, in a strange bed, in a strange room, and neither his mother or father will be there.' I stayed close to my instinct about what might be too much for him, and for me, and suggested we should wait a few more months.

Some days, it was boring. He couldn't yet crawl and I had a cold and was feeling very bleak; he was six months old and only just weaned and it rained all day! The pushchair hadn't got a hood and I didn't feel we could go out. I was bored of playing with him and he was bored of playing with me. I lay on the sofa and laid him down beside me and we both fell asleep.

CHAPTER 2

Nina

NINA, LIKE ME, is a first-time grandmother. Cassia is her youngest child. She also has a son, Adam, soon to have his first baby, and another daughter, Beeban. Having sold her publishing company she now works freelance at many different enterprises. She lives in London within shouting distance of our grandson Cato. Nina and I met through our children, and when Cato was born we didn't know each other well and were not really able to be a comfort to each other during his difficult birth. Since then Cato has brought us together, as has this business of talking about what it's like being grandmothers, and we have become friends.

MY GRANDMOTHER

I don't have any first-hand memories of my grandparents because I came to England as a tiny child during the war, a refugee from Central Europe. My mother and father suffered so much fear and grief that I decided very young to have nothing to do with their past in order, as we say now, to lead my own life. It was only recently, encouraged by Cassia and Roc, that I decided to investigate.

I discovered that my great-grandmother on my mother's side was a scrap-metal merchant in Cracow. She had a street cart and worked all year round, even through the bitter winters. She was the provider for the family, looked after the children and did the housework. She did everything. My grandfather was a religious scholar. It is doubtful whether he did very much, but he led the life. Nevertheless, she always wore an apron in her husband's presence as a sign of respect. In spite of everything she accepted her more lowly position. This is the Orthodox Jewish way.

My father was in England on business when the war broke out. The borders were closed and he was unable to return. I was two years old when my mother, my grandmother, my aunt and her family fled from Belgium to France where we were in hiding for a while. My mother and I were able to get to England via Portugal, but we had to leave the others behind because my grandmother had no papers and therefore couldn't cross frontiers.

I'm told that my grandmother was very devoted to her grandchildren and that she used to save sugar lumps for me in the pocket of her vast apron. My cousin, who shared a bed with her throughout the war, told me that my grandmother often cried at night because she imagined that her sons in Poland had ended up in the extermination camps. These sons were Belser Hasidim, which means they belonged to a fundamentalist religious sect that had turned its back on modern life and rejoiced in the life to come. Despite the difficulties, my grandmother maintained an Orthodox Jewish way of life throughout the war. She even wore a sheitel, that is she shaved her head and wore a wig. She died four days before the liberation of France, just before she would have had her worst fears about her sons confirmed.

It's only recently that I discovered my mother came from a really poor family. She never talked about it. For example, they were so hard up that my aunt had to agree to an arranged marriage to a wealthy man so that our family would be helped financially. The combination of poverty and of pain, loss and displacement during the war was very strong. The only way I could deal with my parents' anguish was to turn away from it. It was only by discovering how poor my mother had been that I realised what it must have meant to her to be well off.

When my mother became a grandmother it coincided with an unexpected downturn in my father's affairs and she suddenly galvanised herself into action. She used to come up the hill to our house with vast shopping bags full of special food and nice things for the children. She was a bounteous grandmother. I catch myself doing what she used to do, going to see Cassia, Roc and Cato with something in my bag! There was my mother, with her shopping bags, and there am I, a lifetime later, having rebelled and so on, with the same shopping bags going up the hill. And I wonder if in the end everything is the same.

※

NINA AND THE BIRTH OF CATO

I think Roc and Cassia have both been wonderful to us in that they haven't been afraid to let us participate in their lives. Roc was very involved in Cassia's pregnancy; I think he was marvellous. When Cassia went into labour, he phoned me and said, 'The baby's on its way and we're very happy!'

When you arrived, Nell, looking lovely and fresh with champagne bottles under your arms, I was amazed. I couldn't have done that! I had problems about Cassia wanting to have the baby at home. I couldn't help thinking, 'What if things go wrong?'

As it turned out, after fourteen or fifteen hours of labour, things looked pretty grim and I got terribly upset when Cassia had to be rushed to hospital. What you don't know and what I've been longing to tell you is that when we were in the waiting room, I got anxious and went to see what I could find out. I went further down the corridor than was permitted and saw the midwife come out of the delivery room with a huge yellow disposal bag. I thought, 'That's it, what am I going to do? I must just sit here till they come and tell us.' A little while later, Roc came out and said, 'It's a little boy and he's sweet,' and I remember his face when he said it. I told Cassia I would never forget how he received his son, the way he held Cato in the delivery room. It was as if he were a little lamb. I found his fatherly bonding with this little lamb very moving. I had a lot of hard times during the delivery . . . [By now both these grandmothers are in tears.]

Nell: I was very frightened.

Nina: I didn't know you were frightened. I felt very alone.

Nell: I thought the best thing was just to try and keep calm.

Nina: There has been a lot of support for having babies at home for all the reasons we know – that hospitals can be very expedient, that it's not always the right atmosphere, but in spite of all that I would have preferred her to have this baby in hospital. People talk about life standing still and I think life stood still for me then when things got really bad. Life stood still. I know that Cassia feels bad now that it was such a difficult time. I think we are victims of the pursuit of the perfect birth. It's a wicked myth and I certainly haven't come across many perfect births; they are all hard in different ways.

NINA AND CATO

I did have a regular day each week when I used to take Cato to his grandfather's house. Although Mike and I are separated, we are still very close and we can enjoy being grandparents together. It was a bit of a re-creation of the old life: we invited mutual friends to lunch and in a way it was how it had been the first time round. There we'd be with old friends and Cato would go from lap to lap!

When Cassia and Roc first had the baby I was willing to cook and shop for them, and clean and generally help. It then became clear that they could perfectly well take that over. So I thought I could do this one day a week. Then one day every week seemed more than I could manage. So now it's all more flexible; sometimes I have him during the week and sometimes at the weekend, or I may baby-sit for them at night if they want to go out together. I see less of him than I did, but I drop in from time to time if I want to see him.

Of course I've got used to seeing him, and I really do want to see him. Every time, there's something new he can do and he's just so lovely. I used to get bored sometimes, stuck at home with my own children, but I never feel that with him. There is also something that involves me more than you: although Roc is a lovely father, as we both know child care does fall more on the mother. Apart from my pleasure in Cato, there is also my daughter's need.

Nell [unable to resist interrupting]: I've noticed that the grandmother whose daughter has the baby is slightly superior towards the mother of the father of the baby. From my point of view, it's an individual relationship with the child and I really don't think that there's a superior relationship with the mother's family. [Lots of laughter]

Nina: Not towards the child, no, but there is also my relationship with Cassia as a young woman having to make some very difficult adjustments. Perhaps I made it more difficult by the way I treated my daughters. I never liked to see the girls in the kitchen, so they went out into the world not knowing how to cook an egg. What I'm saying is that I have sympathy for the business of just coping with the day, so I do things that are not to do with Cato, but are things especially for her. I know you help her too, but obviously she would come more often to me and say, 'I need to sleep; can you have him this afternoon?' I also feel that it's very important for her to be able to go out sometimes, secure that he is being well looked after, so I will baby-sit for her till she finds someone she can trust. I'm happy to do it and that's something specially for her.

It was interesting how things were between Cassia and me when she had the baby. We have always been very close and I imagined that when she had a child we would be brought even closer. To my surprise the opposite happened: the minute she had the baby there was a certain distance. I mean, instantly. And I was shocked because it was so unexpected. Maybe it was just that I had to let the little girl go. It was a good thing, but it was unexpected and painful.

I was put on the spot by Cato's arrival. I was without work, without a home of my own and without material evidence of the life that I had lived. This was probably by unconscious design, but nevertheless, there I was, carrying my life in my shopping bags. What would he make of me? I was upset in the first few months because there he was and I was busy thinking about myself. I was doing everything for him, and I loved him the way he was and he came into the world with so much. But I was grieving about myself. Here is the grandson, but who is the grandmother?

There is a popular myth about what it is to be a grandmother. She is seen to be a woman who has done everything she has to do and is completely ready for her grandchild. And of course it isn't really like that!

Recently I looked after Cato for ten days. Cassia told me there was a family wedding in Austria, and that she'd like to go for the weekend and leave Cato behind. Could I manage to have him? I said, 'Of course!' Then she said, as they were going to be away it would be nice to make it longer, perhaps a week? Having committed myself to the weekend I thought, 'Why not? Might as well give them the break together.' I believe that's very important because, as a young mother you can so easily lose touch with your adult self. You can get lost in your baby. It's terribly important for Cassia to have a relationship with Roc that isn't just based on the child they've had together. So I thought, 'Okay, if I can do it for a weekend, I can do it for a week.'

Then the idea evolved that perhaps they could go to Poland as well and take a look at where Cassia's family came from. When they worked it out, they found that they needed ten days for the whole trip, so what was originally an offer of three days turned into ten days!

The plan was that I should look after Cato in his own house, but there was some terrible mix-up over floor sanding, and I stood there on the Friday they were going and said, 'It looks as if it'll be impossible for me to stay here.'

Cassia said, 'I'm terribly sorry. It doesn't seem to have worked out very well, but I've got to go now to catch the plane.'

Her last-minute instructions to me were, 'By the way, Mum, don't panic! Babies are very strong.' She left at three o'clock, and a few hours later he was covered in spots and I thought, 'I'd better take him to the doctor.' The doctor said she thought it was chickenpox. So here I was with a child who was peaky, had diarrhoea and probably chickenpox, and I had to take him and his luggage to a place that wasn't set up for a baby. The house I was living in had a circular staircase and cupboards full of china. He also decided he didn't like his travelling cot and didn't want to sleep there.

I had to turf my companion out of his own bed and take Cato into the bed. He doesn't have a pillow and he doesn't like bedclothes, but he does like to move around a lot in the night: I would be every which way, parading round the bed, following him with my pillow. In the morning I was dog-tired. 'Well,' I thought, 'ten days of this is going to be very hard indeed,' so I swept Cato up and took him to his grandfather's for the day. Cato is used to being in this house, and it is set up for his visits and after all it *is* his grandfather's house. Immediately he felt a lot better and was happy, and then, of course, I thought, 'If he's happy, I'm happy, and if he's unhappy, I'm totally miserable.' So I rang my friend and said, 'Will you pile all his stuff into a taxi and we'll stay here.'

We put Cato's cot up in the sitting room because that is the room he knew best and the next question was: where shall I sleep? I didn't want to sleep in the same room because his eyes would light on me directly he woke up and yet I didn't want to sleep on the floor above as that was too far away. The long and short of it was that we rolled out a little futon in the bathroom and that's where Granny slept, wedged between lavatory and bath. Granny slept there for the rest of the week and we were actually quite happy; without words, he sorted everything out. He had pushed things in the direction where they made sense to him and he felt secure.

Since then I've looked after him for three days in his own home and that was really very easy. He knew his routine and showed me what it was. For instance, when he gets up in the morning he likes to look at his picture of animals and point at each one while you name it. I took him to the playground. I had resented spending too much time in playgrounds when my own children were young. I used to think my life would ebb out in a playground: I would simply run out of life if I had to sit in many more sandpits! Yet I sit in a sandpit with Cato and it never occurs to me to resent it. Little girls always turn up to play with him.

With my own children I was always thinking about the other things that I could be doing, whereas with Cato I'm completely in the moment, and I can think of nothing better than dressing him and getting him ready to go out. I sit having breakfast with him, just the two of us. One morning we had crumpets instead of toast and he was so excited; I felt life was really good.

I do find him extraordinarily lovely and he has the feel that he could have been my child. He feels right, smells right. That I should have to look after him seems quite appropriate. This is nothing to do with helping out. This is him and me. The danger is that the more I get involved with him the more attached I become. I can't go back to the kind of life where I spend time wondering if the sores behind the ears are getting better, or whether his nappy rash has cleared up. It's not my place to worry about those things any more. I need to do a certain amount to have that close rapport with him, but I don't want to turn it into a dependency, or go back to that point when I was a young mother. I'm not a young mother again and I don't want to be one.

Committing so much time to Cato also stimulates my desire to be alone, to fulfil lots of very neglected internalised plans that I put off. It's as if he were saying to me, 'I could take up most of your time, or you could do with your time what you really feel would be most valuable.'

I think, ultimately, the important thing is, if, when thinking back on his granny, he were able to say, 'She was great!' and also, 'She was very good to me,' in that order. So perhaps one has a responsibility in the first place to be oneself and in the second place to be a caring grandmother. If we get it the wrong way round we could be forgotten altogether. When I had Cato for ten days, Cassia came back and said, 'It was wonderful,' and I felt very good about having enabled her to have a lovely holiday. The next time she went off, she came back and said 'I missed Cato so much; I wish I hadn't gone!' and I began to think, 'If you missed him so much what was I doing!' I don't want to be an infinite resource in the absence of some kind of childminder. If there's a crisis that's something else.

Nell: I have a very adventurous friend who lives in Turkey. She's 73 and still leads tours. She's at the centre of her life and if her grandchildren want to see her they go to her. I have mixed feelings about this whole fact of being a grandmother and wanting to be a reliable grandmother who could be turned to in a crisis, and at the same time wanting to be an unreliable person. Wanting to be spontaneous, wanting to disappear abroad at a moment's notice, not wanting to be the kind of grandmother . . .

Nina: . . . who has her hair in a bun and both hands in the oven gloves . . .

Nell: At the same time I don't want to be disapproved of . . .

Nina: . . . for being flighty and unavailable!

Nell: Yes, for being flighty. I don't know who by . . .

Nina: Yourself! Nobody else is sitting in judgement on you. So perhaps our struggle is not with them, but with ourselves. And I don't think it is all about putting in time, although time does come into it. Obviously an absent grandmother is not the same as somebody who is very present in your life.

I have to decide what I can do and what I want to do. At the end of the day, the one who is good to be with is not necessarily the one who does the donkey work, but the person who is simply good to be with. In the end, I don't suppose we are going to be judged by the number of hours we put in, but by the people we are. Almost unfair, as perhaps all my long hours may not stand me as well with Cato as an afternoon with you! [Lots of laughter]

I feel differently now from how I felt when he was born when I said, 'Here *he* is, but who am *I*?' I know now that if I neglect myself I will be as badly off as if I hadn't put in the hours with him which give me so much pleasure. As he grows up, he'll be more aware of who we are, and what insights we can give him and what directions we have to offer, and, of course, what love we can give. I don't think we should worry about it. I think it's working out.

X

LATER THAT SUMMER

Looking back on it I'm amazed at the anguish I felt around the time of Cato's birth. The other day I saws a Dutch film called *The Polonaise* which struck a cord: one of the themes was that the generation that grew up on the Continent during the war can't get shot of the bad memories or the guilt. The film is centred on a wedding and a lot of pain and madness come through, which have not been accepted by that particular community. It was the happy event of the wedding that sparked off so much pain and, likewise, in my case, I think the happy occasion of Cato's arrival brought with it a lot of distress that had been hived off and hidden. The culture I come from is the culture of non-acceptance: you fight or you are defeated, but you never accept. It seems to me now that you have to accept even the worst things that happen to you if you are to live your life, and that acceptance is positive. That has happened and now we move on. You don't drag it with you.

I now have another grandchild and this time it doesn't seem so complicated. Was it because Cato was the first? This time I don't think I have to justify my whole life. It's just terrific and good fun and I look forward to our getting to know each other.

I think it is marvellous that Cato has established so many happy relationships within the family. I really admire the way his parents see him as an individual who likes a certain way of doing things. They respond to how he feels, which is perhaps why he is so calm. He hasn't had to panic or be very angry. My greatest pleasure is to see him discovering the world, to see him acquire language, see more, further up the wall. The other day he saw a painted horse high up on the wall of his grandfather's house. He hadn't noticed it before. Now he can walk, his horizons have widened. We can talk now, he understands everything.

The other day – it was one of the nicest moments of my life – I took Cato to visit an old friend and we talked all the way home. He had enough experience to understand that we were going home, that he would have a bath, that we would have tea, that we would see Mummy: there was enough there, with a few songs thrown in, to keep talking between Crouch End and the Harrow Road.

Nell [interrupting]: When I drive him home, I just turn on Radio Three and we listen to music.

Nina: When I said to him, 'And then you'll go to bed and we'll say "Goodnight",' he went, 'Puff, puff,' and blew, as if to remind me that when he gets into bed we always blow the mobiles above his cot and that I had forgotten a really important part of going to bed.

I've spent a lot of time in my life getting out of housework, but the irony is that when I look after Cato so much of it is physical: washing and changing, putting things on and taking them off, feeding and cooking and washing up, all that stuff, and perhaps it wasn't so clever to have banished it in the past because it's very pleasurable. I'm reminded how physical bringing up children is and how much I missed it in the years between my children growing up and Cato coming along. It's extraordinary, now that we have it back, to think how we managed without it.

What Cato gives me is the sheer pleasure of living. He reminds me that there isn't so much to it all, that actually a good breakfast, a nice walk, a new word, good weather, a new hat – everything – is just outrageously delightful, and that it's as simple as that, and all those things that take enormous effort are not necessarily where our satisfaction comes from. The greatest surprise for me is that after seeking satisfaction in so many places it can be so easy, so before my nose, and over such simple matters. It is valuing things as they are.

CHAPTER 3

❧

Diana

DIANA IS A *writer. We met in 1957, both already married, two young women jitterbugging at Bohemian parties. Now she lives partly in Wales, where she runs a bed-and-breakfast for fishermen in her tower near the Wye, and partly in London. She is married to George, a touring singer/musician. Her children are Patrick, now dead, Candy and Tom. They live together with Candy's daughter, Katie, in a terraced house off Ladbroke Grove in London. I am very envious of what Diana has created.*

Today, when we meet, the sun is shining and we rattle first through north-west London in her old Ford to collect Katie from her nursery school. Inside, the last three little girls are waiting to go home. Katie bounds towards her granny, with her red plastic lunchbox, and the young teacher tells Diana how good Katie is being this term, how well she has settled down. Diana glows with pride and off we go home.

'Aren't there any boys in your school?' I ask Katie.

'All the boys are dead,' she says.

'Katie!' says her grandmother.

We get back to the house and, while Diana finds the key, Katie climbs precariously up the steep wall with a twelve-foot drop on one side.

'That's what I would find frightening,' I say.

'I do!' she says.

We go in, Diana puts the kettle on, and Katie gets out her colouring book and puts her video of Peter Pan *on the telly. She is four next week and she discusses the plans for her party with her granny. Then she settles down, curled on the bed in Candy's room which is next to the kitchen.*

The house is packed: Tom, Candy and Katie each have their own room, George has a suite in the basement and Diana has turned one end of the large study into a bedsitting room for herself. She has given up being a writer for the moment and instead is being a grandmother and taking care of her family. The house feels very alive with books on the kitchen table and modern paintings all over the walls – alive and fertile. The love between Diana and Katie is sure and easy.

MY MATERNAL GRANDMOTHER

When I was about six years old I met my maternal grandmother for the first and only time. I was in a tube station with my mother during the war and we came across a little old lady who was obviously waiting for us. My mother gave her a ten-shilling note and she went away. I said, 'Who was that?' and my mother said, 'That was your other granny.' My mother lied about her family; there was always a mystery around the subject so I stopped asking questions. Now, of course, I'd love to know, but it's too late, my mother's dead.

MY PATERNAL GRANDMOTHER

My father's mother was called Auntie Smudge and I lived with her for most of the war. My father was away in the army and my mother was away somewhere too, I'm not quite sure where. I was a weekly boarder at a convent school and I spent the weekends with my granny. She lived in north London in a huge Finchley house, with two or three rooms on each floor, and she had lodgers. She was a Victorian style of woman, quite strict. I remember her coming in to say 'Goodnight', and my hands were under the covers and she said, 'Hands always have to be outside the bedclothes.' She was also loving and kind. I remember her only once being very angry because I ran away from her in a shop. I was about seven and had a little friend with me and we thought it would be fun to run away, so we did! My granny must have been petrified. I saw more of my grandmother than I did of my mother. Sometimes we used to sleep in the cellar together alongside the coal if there was an air raid.

When the war was over and my father came back, we went to live in Essex leaving my grandmother in London. I did grow away from her, but that was more because I rejected all my family. It was a class thing, they were too common. I thought that if I wanted to get on I'd be better off without them. And I think I was probably right – it was true in those days, wasn't it? Later, when I was seventeen and I had Patrick, my aunt looked after him for some time and my grandmother lived opposite, although she was quite old by that time.

I do remember that she was very important to me. She never made a fuss of me, but she brought me up and she was there. She had a very strong moral code and I wouldn't have wanted to offend it in any way because I felt it was right: things like, if you promised something you did it, and you didn't let people down and you did a decent day's work for God and country. I went on seeing her till she died.

MY GRANDDAUGHTER KATIE

Candy was living with me in the tower near Brecon and the baby was very late. We were sitting watching television and she said, 'I think it's started.' We rang up the hospital and they said, 'Well, you can pack a bag and come in if you like.' So we drove in. It was this wonderful starry night, the September that was very, very hot and the night was cool and clear. When we got there they examined Candy and said nothing would happen for ages and would we like a room for the night? They put us in a lovely room with two beds and tea and coffee and a radio – it was like a hotel – and I went to sleep.

I remember getting up in the night and massaging Candy's back and her feet, as she was beginning to feel the contractions. At about eight o'clock in the morning the midwife examined Candy again and said it was still going to be ages. Candy told me she couldn't bear not having any knickers on, and I thought this is probably the one time in your life when you don't need knickers, but she wanted me to get her some. So I rushed home. I was gone for twenty minutes and when I got back she was in strong labour and the baby was born twenty minutes later.

There were the nurse, the midwife and me, and we were still in the bedroom because the delivery room was full, because two other mothers were giving birth at the same time. The midwife had wet hair because she was the emergency midwife and when they rang her she had been in the shower. Then, as Katie was coming out, the midwife called out, 'Quick, the cord's round her neck three times!' and I thought I was going to die on the spot. Then I saw Katie's head and she was bright purple. I'd never seen a baby being born before and I was terrified. The midwife put her finger under the cord and the nurse cut and tied it, and then out she popped.

I was totally stunned and overcome, I had no idea it would be so wonderful. I was completely involved in Candy; I felt incredibly moved by her experience of birth and all my feelings were to do with her. I didn't care about Katie.

Candy didn't have to have stitches, and after a bit she

went to sleep and I went home. It was the most beautiful day, and I sat in the garden and felt absolutely desperate. I had no one to celebrate with and I didn't know what to do with myself. George was away in Ireland and Tom was in Scotland somewhere and I couldn't ring the father of the baby because I didn't know him. I quite understood why the father goes down the pub and everyone buys him a drink. I needed something like that. There was no one to share it with. I rang a few friends and then, as the day progressed and I had no more friends to ring, I started ringing friends in Australia and America, and at last got hold of Tom and that was a great relief. Three days later she was home.

I think if you have an unmarried daughter who has a child, it's a very close relationship. Someone told me that the mother of a daughter who gives birth to a daughter is the closest kind of grandmother you can get.

The house had been very geared to this baby and here she was. Candy always says how lucky she was. She lay in bed and was waited on by me and Tom and Yvette, our cleaning lady who adores babies. The baby slept with Candy at night so she had to wake and feed her then, but in the daytime Katie came downstairs so Candy could get a lot of sleep, and I know you're not meant to say this, but Katie was a good baby and only woke when she needed feeding. I remember very clearly, it was when she was six weeks old, I suddenly thought, 'I've fallen in love!' I hadn't felt it before then, but you know when you fall in love that awful lurching feeling, that stomach-turning-over feeling, I suddenly had it with Katie. It wasn't love at first sight. Around about this time Candy moved to her own place, but I often had Katie for the night when Candy went out. Then later they both came to live with us.

In May, when she was about eight months old, I took her to Greece for a fortnight. It was lovely! She'd sleep till 7.30, then she'd go back to bed from eleven till one and have her afternoon sleep from three to four, then bed again at seven, so there was plenty of time for me to read and relax.

I found she was very manageable up until about two years old. All she wanted to do was to be loved and smiled at and talked to, and to join in, and then an ego developed. All of a sudden she became aware that she had a say in things and her own personality: 'I want!' She didn't understand why she couldn't have everything she wanted and it was really quite a battle. When someone rang up I'd say, 'I can't talk, I'm looking after Katie.' But in the last six months, since she's turned three, it's been much easier. She doesn't like it if I'm on the telephone, but at least now I can say to her, 'If you don't let me talk on the telephone then I'm not going to read you a story,' and that's the end of it.

I found looking after her came very naturally. I can't say it did when I was a mother, but it did this time round. I think, I hope, that I've become much less selfish. It seems to me that when you're young, you're married and you've got children, there are just so many demands on you: to go out, to give dinner parties, to be made up, to be sexy. The whole thing was exhausting. Now when I'm looking after Katie that's all I'm doing.

Sometimes the responsibility gives me nightmares. I find it quite terrifying. The river is a good fifteen minutes' walk away across two fields. She'd have actually to run away to decide to go down to the river. Yvette has a daughter called Rachel who is eleven and when she comes to play with Katie, Katie says 'Let's go down to the river.' I did let them go once; it was a lovely sunny day and it seemed awful that they couldn't walk across the field. I said, 'You must only be gone fifteen minutes.' Of course they weren't back and I went haring down to the river expecting to see two floating bodies. They were playing happily, and really you can only be as careful as you can. It can't wreck your life or their lives. Unfortunately as you get older you see the dangers more and it's one of the advantages of being a young mother that you don't.

I don't have much regret about being older, being a grandmother. I'm actually happier now than I've ever been in my life. I'm better at being a grandmother than I was at being a mother. I think I've only changed because I'm older, not for any other reason. I think it would be pathetic if I hadn't changed at my age! I still like now and then to have the chance to get dressed up and put make-up on and see if I can look glamorous, but, my God, if I had to do it every day I couldn't bear it. You're not attractive to men in the same way, I'm aware of that. I've got much bossier and much more forthright; although they do say that it isn't that women become more bossy as they get older, it's just that when they're younger and hoping to be attractive to men they suppress all that bossiness, and then when they stop bothering it all comes out!

I'm very firm with Katie; I'd say I was much stricter than Candy is. Candy is more happy-go-lucky, she likes to sit and cuddle her. I get her to do what I want by a mixture of threats and bribes. She really hates to see me angry, she just can't bear it. I remember Patrick, Candy and Tom used to be terrified of what they called 'my look'. If there was a lunch party, and I thought they were getting too cheeky and were going to say something that would embarrass me, then I'd give them this 'look' which said, 'Don't chance your luck!' And usually it would work. Katie is less frightened of 'the look', and indeed will even imitate it and give it right back to me. Once or twice I have been very angry with her. I'll raise my voice and tell her how angry I am, but I've never smacked her properly, just the occasional pat on the bottom. Now I say, 'If you don't do what I say, you won't go to *The Witches*, or you won't get a story.'

The other day I picked her up from a friend's house; she didn't want to leave and so she was sulking in the car. We were driving back to the house and I said, 'Katie, it's really boring you sulking like this, and you might find when you come out of this sulk and you want to talk to me, your sulk has put me in such a bad mood that *I* shall be sulking, so you will want to talk and you won't have anyone to talk to.' Indeed this is exactly what happened; when we got home, she came out of the sulk and started talking and I wouldn't speak to her. I was trying to show her that it isn't very nice when people don't answer you.

I was quite lazy about my children and couldn't be bothered to be rational, because it takes quite a lot of time. I think about Katie a great deal. I get angry when she makes a fuss about things like going to bed, but she's really a very easy child. She has her own room and Candy has hers. We have our meals together. In some ways it's very nice for Katie, though it's less nice for Candy. Katie has got Tom, who she sometimes likes to think of as her daddy. She'd never say it to me because she knows it's not true and that I might accuse her of lying, but she'll say to the other children, 'Tom's my daddy.' She's also got George, who worships her; he's coming and going and buying her presents and spoiling her. But for Candy it's not so nice, because she wants her independence and her own life and her own saucepans. It's not so nice living under the shadow of your mother. I got married at sixteen to get away from all that.

Now Candy is planning to live with two friends, one of whom has a child a little older than Katie. They are all going to get a flat together. The three grown-ups are each going to have a room of their own and the two children are going to share a room. I feel anxious about it. It seems to me incredibly difficult for people with children to manage on very little money. I also worry about Katie sharing a room with another child when she's had four years of a room of her own. And I feel jealous that Katie will become very close to these other two people in the flat and in some way less close to me. Sometimes I feel quite desperate at the idea of them leaving and then I think, well, in some ways it will be rather nice for me. There'll be more room in the house and it can be quite tiring looking after a small child. Of course, I'll still see a lot of her; they're not going to Australia, more likely Kensal Rise! Then there are the holidays; if Candy remains a working mum, I'm not going to be short-changed as regards child care!

I don't find any complications about financial support, although maybe Candy does because she probably wishes she were self-supporting. I think it's very hard for young people these days. It's particularly hard if you're a single mother, but George earns quite a lot, so it would seem to me quite ludicrous if either Tom or Candy had to pay for things while they're living at home, they're just part of the household. Tom is very good at cooking and shopping, so he contributes like that. Candy doesn't cook so much because she works long hours, but she does other things in the house and she types for George. George pays for Katie's nursery school.

I want it above board. When Candy and Katie move away, I don't want to be filling up the coffers now and again; I want Candy to say, 'Look, I can do this, this and this, but I haven't got enough left to do this. Can you help me with it?' Otherwise it's a bottomless pit. But if you choose what it is you want to do, maybe pay the school fees and the telephone bill, it's George and my choice what we do. I think it needs to be something quite definite and then everyone knows where they are.

I don't have conflicts with Candy about Katie's upbringing. I sometimes think it's incredibly irritating for Candy if Katie's eating her Haunted House and I say, 'Katie, eat up properly and take your feet off the table.' Candy might be more inclined to let it go, but I feel that it's my kitchen. Until about a year ago I used to be more tentative and careful, and I don't think it was very successful, so now I just get on with it and do it. If it irritates Candy, I'm sorry about it, but there it is, I suppose she has to lump it. Sometimes, because I'm the matriarchal figure in the house, when people are asking questions, including questions about Katie, they refer the question to me and I think that must be irritating for Candy.

LATER THAT AUTUMN,

About a month ago Candy said, "Mum, would it be all right if I stayed on; I realise I can't afford to move yet.' I was thrilled because it seemed to me sensible of her in many ways. Why should she go and struggle in a flat with very little money, trying to pay rent, bills, child care, nursery school, clothes, running a car to get Katie to school . . . ? I know thousands, millions of women do it, but Candy hasn't done it and she hasn't got to, so what was the point? The point was obviously for her to have her own independence and freedom, but I think those are things you can have at home and you can have them through being responsible and caring. You negotiate them with your family. At the moment she can have a bit of fun giving Katie treats. She can buy her nice clothes, which she loves to do, and take her to the zoo. It doesn't have to be Granny who provides all the treats; it's almost the other way round. Granny provides the baked beans and the Ribena and Mummy can afford the treats!

Before Katie came to Greece on holiday with me, Candy

took her to stay with friends in the Outer Hebrides. It cost quite a lot of money, but they had a wonderful holiday. If she were scraping and saving in her own flat, they wouldn't be able to afford holidays like that. Candy is going to take a week off unpaid for Katie's half-term, but if she had the rent to pay she couldn't take a week off. I think staying on with us is the right decision for now, although we're quite a lot of people in a not very big house!

It's the third year running I've taken Katie to Patmos. This year was specially nice: I've always taken a house before so that the rest of the family could come too, but this year I thought, 'It's ridiculous, I spend my life running houses, when I go on holiday it ought to be to a hotel.' So we stayed in a hotel and a friend of mine who's got a little girl six months older than Katie came too. Her boyfriend, who I get on well with, came for the first week and after that it was the four of us.

It was idyllic. Every day is the same: blue sky and sunshine, breakfast of yoghurt and honey, and then going down to the port and getting on a boat and going to a beach. Then it's lying there and watching the little girls learn to swim. Katie's very brave and, I might say, insubordinate! Her character is rebellious, which has its good side because she's adventurous, she'll climb a mountain and take her armbands off in the sea. In the evenings we'd go to cafés to eat, because in Greece everyone eats with their children and they can run around outside. There are no cars and it's so different from here. The children really opened out.

Sometimes I was worried, because Katie likes to run off and she doesn't care if I'm out of sight, but I always dressed her in very gaudy colours so I could spot her a mile off. She and Ruby, the other little girl, would love these Greek men with long thick beards, and they would approach them and say, 'You remember me, don't you!' Greek men enjoy children; they aren't frightened of them like so many English men and they'd play silly games with them.

As soon as I got back, although I was looking forward to it, I immediately felt hemmed in, but you can't be on holiday all the time. Katie's an only child, so she had a host of imaginary friends and it's no longer true that she has to be occupied. She's had a lot of attention and she's always been responded to immediately; I feel it's paid off and now she's very self-sufficient.

Nell: I have the same thing with Cato as I had with my children. I don't really enjoy playing, but I love the 'presence'. I liked the Drop-In Centre because there was so much for him to do and I could just sit on a chair watching. I'm not very good at helping him build bricks.

Diana: I hate most of the playing, but I love the doll's house.

Nell: Oh, that's a good idea. I'd love a doll's house! I'm going to get a doll's house for me and Cato.

Diana: I don't mind playing with the farm either.

Nell: Perhaps I'll get a farm instead!

Diana: The sort of game Katie sometimes wants to play now are games like Snap which I don't much like.

Nell: No, I don't like cards, I don't like any games, but I like bus rides.

Diana: Yesterday Katie and I went to a huge shop called IKEA out on the North Circular Road. As you go in, there's a children's play centre and the first room is full of coloured balls, tiny little balls, and the children take their shoes off and just fall in these balls. Then there's a big nursery with paints and toys and someone in charge, and you write your name down and go off shopping, and if your child gets fed up you hear coming over the loud speaker, 'Will Mrs Melly please come to the play centre, Katie is now anxious to go home!' But I've never had to go back for Katie till I've finished shopping, so outings are fun.

Last week we drove from Wales to London and I looked up a pub in a good-food-in-pubs guide: we found one where you had to cross the Wye on a little footbridge and it was almost like being back in Greece, she could play about while I rested. I'd told her that we'd only got the old car and the journey would take about five hours and then we planned it together, what colouring books she might take and so on. Now we can have proper conversations, we can talk about the past and the future, so it's becoming real companionship between us. I remember how difficult she was between about eighteen months and three. She was very demanding, and needed looking after and occupying the whole time. Now all that has changed and she's really easy company.

It's important to get out, but you'll find as soon as Cato's old enough to try and help you with whatever you're doing you must let him. There's a great temptation to think 'No, she can't do that, so there's no point in letting her try,' but you don't learn things by magic, you only learn things by trying and failing, whether it's doing up your shoes or whatever. And now that Katie can do these things, she can sometimes actually be a help and not just by clearing up her own mess. With the bed-and-breakfast people at the tower in Wales, I can say, if I'm frying eggs, 'Katie, please could you take this toast in.' And she's very happy to carry the toast to the tables.

I don't know why, but I'd forgotten about the learning process. When you're grown-up and you decide to learn how to do something, you work it out, but when you're a child it takes longer and you're always trying to do things you can't do. There is nothing you can do when you're born, so you must always let children try. If they say, 'I can do it,' then, as long as you don't have to catch a bus, you must let them try and they will become self-sufficient so much more quickly. Katie has got some black pull-on shoes like mine and for her to get those on is a bit more complicated than her Velcro-strap ones, so I started saying, 'Katie, those are too difficult for you; I'll do them.' And then she quite rightly said, 'I know, Granny, but I can try.' Two days later she could do it by herself, which saves me the fag of having to put them on for her!

When Katie was born, Candy was living with me for the first two months and then she moved into a little cottage of her own in Brecon. I remember feeling quite sad about that, knowing how much I would miss Katie, but I didn't feel and have never felt any jealousy about Candy. Candy told me she'd asked one of her friends to baby-sit one night. I knew she hadn't asked me because she'd have had to bring Katie out to me and I felt a first pang of jealousy then: somebody else was going to be looking after Katie. Once or twice she would say a relation on Candy's father's side was going down for the weekend, a half-aunt or uncle of Katie, and I felt miserable with jealousy. It doesn't happen any more because now I feel so confident in my relationship with Katie, but it's new in not happening. I think it was straightforward human jealousy. When you have a husband or a child, you have an exclusive relationship with them. You want to be the only one or at least the most important one; with your child you're the only mother and with your husband you're the only wife. If there are other wives, then you're jealous of them. With your grandchild, the exclusivity of that relationship is harder to get at. I'm lucky, I'm the only grandmother; the other one is out of the picture.

Nell: What I experienced when Cato was born was a sense of displacement – in not being actually his mother.

Diana: Yes, however bad one was at it, one had still been the only mother for one's children.

Nell: With a grandchild, it meant adjusting to a place that was real and satisfying and comfortable, and perhaps what it comes to is making your own completely individual, independent relationship with the child, and then it endures through thick and thin. If you do go off to Timbuktu for a year and a day, when you come back you are still that same person and you take up the relationship again, because it isn't the child's relationship with anyone else, it is her connection with you. In a way, this butts on to something which I really want to take care of, which is to remain myself in my relationship with Cato rather than be 'the wonderful grandmother'. Instead I want to remain myself and if I'm feeling gloomy that day to be able to say, 'I feel really bored.' I want to stay true to me, rather than be 'wonderful Granny'.

Diana: I feel I have to make a bit more of an effort. I think I do actually want to be a wonderful granny!

Nell: I want to be wonderful, but first I want to be me, and to show him the things that I'm interested in. It's so important for me to remain me, because I so easily become someone else and then I'm miserable.

Diana: I feel almost the opposite. I like being pushed into situations where I'm not myself, because myself tends to sit at home with my apron on feeling a bit gloomy! [Lots of laughter] Whereas if I actually have to make an effort, I might find I was pushed into taking the dogs for a walk in Richmond Park like you, and it was very nice and I was actually enjoying it! I enjoy being 'taken out of myself' – I think that's the expression, isn't it? If I'm depressed I make an effort to hide it and hope it will pass off.

We have supper together about three evenings out of four, but if you have supper with the people you are living with, it doesn't mean you spend the whole evening together. Katie has her supper at 6.30 and she's in bed about eight. Candy always baths her, and reads to her and gives her her supper. When Candy comes home from work, that's what she's doing, taking care of Katie. If Candy was rushing home from work, picking up Katie from a childminder, facing a pile of washing, the flat to clean and supper to make – I know people do it, but . . .

Nell: . . . it's pretty good hell. What do you feel about still being the centre of the household, the linchpin of this family? Having brought up a family, you're not now finding yourself riding through Turkey on a camel, free as air. I often think about this, because I think I'm someone who finds living for the sake of living and enjoying it for its own sake very difficult, which is probably why I write books. I think I pushed my children out too soon; I wanted everything tidied up and organised. Reuben said to me not long ago, 'Mum, you'll bury me before I'm dead just to get it over and done with!' I didn't see then how it is the fabric of life that is so important. I saw life more as the sum of what you had achieved and I didn't feel I had achieved enough just to be a mum who enjoyed her children.

Diana: I don't know if all this is so different for me because my eldest son Patrick died. Perhaps I so like having Candy and Tom around because of that, or maybe they haven't been able to leave because of that. A mother is not the only person affected by a death in the family. The others have been strongly affected . . . and yet how could Tom leave as a young actor? Economically it would be very hard indeed.

I said to Katie after we got back from Wales when she wanted me to climb a tree, 'Oh Katie, I'm just an old granny and they don't have to do that kind of thing,' and she got upset and said, 'Don't say you're old; if you say you're old that means you're going to die.' I said, 'Not for a long time!' and she said, 'But I want you to say you never will.' And then we have to go through the whole thing that it will be when Katie's grown-up and perhaps she'll have children herself or maybe she'll be a doctor and be able to help people live longer. She isn't talking as an unhappy child, she's just trying to get to grips with it. It's all to do with growing up. 'How long will it be till I grow up?' It's all really trying to understand how things work.

Nell: I envy you living with Katie and yet, bloody hell,

you've been cleaning the crumbs off the kitchen table for twenty-five years . . .

Diana: . . . *thirty*-five years! Well, I feel very, very content at the moment, so obviously I don't mind that much. If I was completely on my own with quite a bit of money, my fantasy is that I'd travel, but I'd probably be perfectly miserable without them. This is what I'm stuck with in a sense and it is very nice. Two years ago I went to southern India with Tom; we travelled around on buses and trains for three months and I did miss Katie a lot. Three months is only three months and I feel I can do that again any old time. I went to Australia last winter and on the way I went to Thailand and travelled a bit.

When I don't have anyone to leave or to come back to, it won't be quite so much fun, will it? I've never been someone completely on my own and I can't imagine what it will be like . . .

CHAPTER 4

Joy

JOY WAS MARRIED at sixteen and had her son Kenny at seventeen.
She is now divorced. Kenny lives with Sharon and they have a
son, Wayne, and by the end of this chapter they have a daughter
too.

'Oh, isn't he beautiful, wonderful . . .'

We are in the maternity ward to visit the day-old baby, her first
grandson. We leave and go to the dilapidated council flats. We ring
for the lift, which doesn't come, and a gritty wind blows dust in
our eyes. The lift still doesn't come. 'Let's walk,' I say. We go to
the staircase and look up over the banisters: twelve storeys of
concrete stairs. We look at each other. Joy is wearing very high
heels. We laugh, she touches my arm. 'Do you want to know how
I really feel? I wish that I was thirty again and that I could get
out of this, run right away from it all . . . Be in love and run
away!'

I first saw Joy in Roehampton; I was on my Lambretta. She
stood out on the grass in her bedroom slippers, her hair in a little
blonde ponytail, shouting at my pillion passenger, her brother. She
was eighteen and I was twenty-three. The following week we made
a date to go out, and went to a pub that played music. She wore
a backless black dress back to front. Her legs were bare, we danced.
It was 1960 and later that summer we took our small sons to a
caravan she had at Selsey.

Now thirty years later we are still friends and have both had our first grandchildren within three months of each other.

MY MATERNAL GRANDMOTHER

My grandfather was a German Jew. He was a short man with a bald head. My grandmother was from the Smart's Circus family and she was pretty and petite. I take after her. My grandmother had sixteen children and my mother was the baby, the same as I was the baby in our family, and when my grandfather died my grandmother came to live with us. She was very old and she shared a room with me and my mum. She had the single bed and me and Mum had the double. My mum wouldn't sleep with my dad no more because she had too many children.

Granny had long silver hair. Her name was Maud. She had a bun and she put big silver hairpins in it. She always wore a pretty crossover apron and a blouse. Although she had had all those children she was a little woman, very dainty. She used to go to the pub and get a jug of beer. She liked her drink, but she was always spotlessly clean and she'd scrub the kitchen floorboards till they were pure white. I didn't like it when she got really old because she used to dribble when she was eating her dinner. I used to tell her stories about what was going on. She was always in the pawnshops if she got a chance to get a bit of beer money. In the end she fell in the fire and got burnt and we had to put her in a home.

THE BIRTH OF MY GRANDSON

Sharon come to me with pains and, seeing as she's always got this wrong with her and that wrong with her, I didn't take much notice. Anyway she says, 'I've got this terrible backache.' She does put a lot on, but it was quarter to two in the morning and Kenny was out, so I says, 'Oh, I don't know, I'd better take you in.'

Well, they put the monitor on her and I says to her, 'The pains aren't that strong yet; I can see on the screen they're only little ones.' We were in the labour ward, just me and her, not a nurse in sight, and she says, 'Don't make me laugh, it hurts,' and I says, 'Well, you'd better laugh now, you'll be crying in a minute,' and then it started.

She swore at the nurse and the nurse said, 'Don't you speak to me like that,' and she's run out and left Sharon with me, and I sat there from three o'clock. She kept screaming! I cuddled her round her neck and she shrieked, 'Help me! Do something for me!' She nearly choked me. And I says, 'This is one time I can't do something for you.'

The place was so busy, babies being born every five minutes, husbands fainting on the floor, not a nurse in sight, I fucking didn't know where I was! She was shrieking like a lunatic, and then I could just about see a little bit of his head and all of a sudden he was sliding out. I shouted out, 'Nurse!' and there he come . . . and there he was . . . he was there . . . literally in my hands, all red, green, blue, yellow, all colours. The nurse come running in and she shouted, 'Ring the bell, ring the bell!' but I'd got the baby and I couldn't reach the bell, so she's got hold of the baby and I'm kissing Sharon and the nurse is saying, 'Get this!' 'Do that!' 'In the cupboard!'

I was wore out, but it was the excitement, the experience, I couldn't have missed, and there he was. I cried, but I wasn't crying; the tears were just pouring out of my eyes. I held him, and then she wrapped him in a green cloth and I give him to Sharon . . . and there he was. It's a wonderful experience – watching it, not having it!

Two days later I felt really depressed. I don't know what it was. Nobody wanted me. The baby was in the hospital, my Kenny was sharp with me. I was lost. Once she brought him home it was different. I knew where I was and each day, he's two weeks old now, I've got closer to him. Specially now she's not feeding him no more. I told her her milk was no good.

I don't think my Kenny likes being a breadwinner. He wants me to look after everything. And I'm not a lover of it either, I'm not used to that sort of thing. I can give much more from my heart when I know someone's looking after me. When I was with Don, he was the breadwinner and I could respond to him. I could get more out of him, so I could give more. I like a man that will look after you. If they can't look after me I don't want them.

Wayne lays on my bed, I make a little nest for him out of my heart pillows. One I put right at the back of him so he feels something. That's what he needs. He needs the touch and the feel of something. I'm going to buy him blue pillow-cases so when I take him out in the pram they'll know he's a boy and not a girl. You know all those frilly heart cushions you give me that I've got on my bed? Well, I put all those around him on my bed and, oh, he looks beautiful, Nell! They should have a kick, they should let the air get to them. I know they can't see, but he's looking all round my room. I say, 'Hello, my darling,' and I know he knows me and I cuddle him up. I have him for the afternoon when I come back from work, but I don't mind, I'm getting a lot of pleasure, although he's only two weeks old. I'm getting no pleasure anywhere else and he is my pleasure!

I've said to her, 'You've got a fridge, you've got a steril-iser, you've got everything you need. Make up your bottles, at least three.' I've upped his food. He was crying all the time, he was hungry, poor little sod. He's better now. I went and got this new stuff for colic. I said, 'Go round and get a bottle of that!' She takes a fucking month of Sundays to go round the corner. Anyway, by the time she comes back I've got him settled.

I sing to him, Nell, and I love him. I've never loved anyone so much. The baby's my life now. He's my new life. I've never loved like this. I'm only sorry she and him aren't getting on. I've stuck up for her and stuck up for her. My Kenny looks like a man of forty now. He's got black rings under his eyes. He's better with the baby than she is. He had a drink the other night and when he went home she thought he was drunk. He said he made out he was, but he wasn't. He said, 'I took the baby and I was making a bottle. "Well, you shouldn't hold him with the kettle in your hand." Mum, I wouldn't let anything happen to that baby.'

You want to see him change the nappy! I didn't think my Kenny had it in him! Saturday, he come over to me Saturday morning; he's got three bottles made up, a pile of napkins in the pram. He loves that baby, but he doesn't love her. True to God, as I sit in this chair. He come to me, he doesn't want her. He's told her and he's told me. It's terrible, she does not shut up. He says, 'Mum, all I ask for is a clean shirt and my dinner when I come home.'

She says to me, 'I'm not a housewife,' and I've said, 'I'm afraid you're going to have to be Nick the Bottlewasher, my love, because you've got that baby to look after!'

So my mate Chrissie says, 'You're too soft with her, you should have fucking told her properly!'

I said, 'I can't, Chrissie, I'm not made that way!'

So she says, 'When I see her I'm going to tell her. So what does she do all day?'

'Nothing! I went round there the other afternoon, she's still got her nightgown on, it's got a tear in it. I says, "Who done that?"

"Kenny!"

"What do you mean, Kenny done it?"

"I told him to hold the baby, he was screaming, while I made the bottle."

"Now I did tell you, Sharon, the other day, if you had made the bottles up at the same time like I told you – you don't wait for that baby to cry before you make the bottle – then when you know the baby's due to wake up, you put it in hot water. As soon as he wakes up, let him cry for a couple of seconds to get his lungs going and then he has his bottle!"

"Well," she says, "I'm depressed."

"I know you are, darling, and look at your face, it ain't even made up. You're home all day long. Now listen to me, if your mother was alive she'd make you wash and dress yourself. You've got no make-up on." '

I said to Chrissie, 'She looks as scruffy as arseholes.' Now I've bought her a suit, lovely suit, navy-blue and white. I said, 'Get yourself a belt and put it round it because it's a bit long, and make yourself up.'

Kenny wants her to go; he says she can have the flat, and I've said, 'That's not fair, Sharon, the home was made for you and it's up to you to make it a bit better. The baby don't take up all your time. I was early-morning cleaning when I had Kenny and I was only seventeen.'

So she says, 'He starts when he comes in!'

And I says, 'He will start if he sees your face like that and you're not made up, any man would start!' And I looked at her and the milk was coming through and I said, 'Why haven't you got pads on you? Or dose it up with cotton-wool!' And she looks at me as if I'm fucking nuts and that was that. So I said to her, 'Don't bath him in the morning, top and tail him in the morning and bath him at night.' Anyway what do you think he did? He had his last feed at twelve o'clock and slept till six!

I said, 'That baby knows when you start arguing, so don't

[44]

argue.' I said to Kenny, 'Don't argue in front of that baby!' So he says, 'Well tell her, Mum.' So I've said, 'You get Kenny's dinner ready like any other wife does and let him feed the baby if he wants to. Let him do the baby and you get on with the dinner. You should have had it prepared before he came home and if he starts arguing, go in the other room and do some ironing. Stay away from him until he calms down.'

My Kenny says, 'She's a right wicked cow, what she says!'

And she said to me, 'I can kill him in one minute with my tongue!'

I don't know what she says, Kenny won't tell me, but he come over to me the other night and he says, 'Mum, I'm not going home no more.' And I says, 'What about that baby?' And he's phoned me later and he's said, 'Mum, I'm home! I've come home for you and that baby.' And I couldn't believe it. And he said, 'I only love you and my baby.' That's the words he said. And I said, 'You're drunk!' And he said, 'No, I'm not drunk, Mum, you're the only two I care about. I cannot stand her; I get nothing from her.'

I explained to him. She's got no mum and dad. Her mum died when she was fourteen. Her dad died two weeks before the baby was born. She's had it hard, but she can't keep playing on that! She's got everything: my three-piece suite, a nice modern television, a stereo. Anyway, yesterday morning I go in there, and she's in her nightgown again and I says, 'Why aren't you dressed at twelve o'clock? You only just got up?' I was fucking wild. The baby was clean, I've got to say that. He had on his lovely little suit what I gave him. So she said, 'No.' The ironing board's in the kitchen, oh my God!

'There are plenty of girls have babies!' I told her. Then he starts crying, so I went round and bought this special dummy. 'He's not having a dummy,' she says. So I say, 'Now listen, Sharon, your milk's no good; he's on the bottle and that baby needs a bit of comfort, so give it to him.' So I bought this latest dummy, with a special teat so you don't get no air and it's good for his gums.

Anyway, into his mouth went the dummy and he stops crying, and I've got him wrapped up like a little Eskimo and he's beautiful! He's lost all that redness, and I spit on my finger and twist his hair round to make a little curl. He hasn't got a lot of hair, but what he has got I'm going to train it from a little baby so he's got curly hair. He looks beautiful, he hasn't got a mark on him, not a mark. I bought him a sailor suit last week. He did look lovely in it. It was only four pounds ninety-nine. I brought him white socks, little tiny white socks. I was fed up with his fucking bootees falling off, and I turned them down, like that. Do you know, I'm not exaggerating, the gear I've bought that baby, I never knew I bought that much. He's got a great big wicker basket, one of them laundry baskets, and it's full up.

I don't let Sharon know what I do, but when I have him over there on my own I puts Lulu [the dog] on the settee on one side and the baby on the other side, and I have one arm round each and I say, 'You're both my babies; you're my baby girl, and you're my baby boy.' And when I took him out in the pram, Lulu walked beside me, she was so proud. I went round to the shop, and I put the brake on and said to Lulu, 'Now sit there and wait till I come out,' and I went in and got my bottle of milk and my packet of fags, and as I stand here, that dog didn't move. So I said, 'I'm going to get you a treat,' and I went back in and bought her a packet of Maltesers!

When I went over the other day he was wearing something I didn't like and I said, 'Where did you get that thing from?' And she said, 'Well, you told me not to dress him till I went out.' But no way will I have anything discoloured on my baby. So I said, 'Well, don't put that on him; it makes him look scruffy. Don't bring him over to me looking like that.'

Fucking hell! He's got beautiful hands – his hands are elegant. And I roll his little sleeves back and she says, 'Oh, he looks different now,' and he did look different. Anyway, I bought some beautiful little blankets what I got from Oxfam, with big thick fringes and a big white crochet one.

When they were getting on all right, Kenny was sharp with me and they didn't want to know. I was frightened to pick him up, but now I just pick him up when I want. I've been through nine months of them constantly arguing. I've carried that baby with her, you know that? I've carried that baby with her, and it seemed as if I'd had so much of her and the job and I just wanted to run away from the whole lot, even the baby! I think it's too tight the way she puts the napkin on. She does it skintight on this stomach. He does like my bed. He peed all over the pillow, but I didn't give a sod!

I said, 'What are you doing over here?'

'I've got to pick her up at the train station.'

'What in this bloody wind, at this time of night? That baby's not six weeks old yet!'

When it gets on top of me, I want to run away; it seems to be draining me. I don't know what it is!

The next morning I goes over because I wanted a bit of sea grass to finish a chair I was caning; this is twelve o'clock in the morning.

'Where's Sharon?'

He said, 'She's upstairs.'

'Surely she's not still in bed?'

'She is, Mum!' So he's shouted out 'Sharon, me mum's here!'

It doesn't half look nice, his kitchen, you'd be ever so proud of him. I've given him my big pine table. So when she brought him down he was red hot! I said, 'What's he doing in that little suit? That was for when he was first born,

[47]

he weighs nine pounds now!' So I says, 'Where's all those lovely suits I bought him?'

'I'm tired.'

I says, 'Tired? It's twelve o'clock!' And I laughed, because I never say too much, I've learnt to hold me tongue.

'Well, he's had his feed and he won't go to sleep.'

'Did you find out about the Farley's I told you about?' I said it nicely, not domineering. 'You give him a quarter in the morning and a quarter in the night-time; he's crying because he's hungry.'

'He only does it when he sees you.'

So I laughed and I said, 'That's because I pick him up.' So I've took him and undone all the back of him, and I said, 'This is ever so tight, love. Where are all those lovely turquoise ones I bought him?' So she fetches one and we dress him up, but she hadn't combed her hair nor nothing – slummucky as arseholes. I never interfered, on my life, but she wanted me to fetch this and fetch that. Here it goes, I thought, skivvy again.

I bought the microwave out of the book; that's their Christmas present. I haven't paid for it yet, but never mind. I said to her, 'Now, when I go, put him up in the bedroom and let him sleep so he's not disturbed by the television.' I said, 'Shall I take the cradle up the stairs?' So I takes the cradle up to the bedroom – bed hadn't been made – and down I come and Chrissie had bought him a beautiful gold St Christopher's medal. I took it out of my bag and gave it to her in its little box and she didn't even look at it, just put it on the side: fifty-odd pound that was. So I said, 'Ta ta, love, have a nice dinner and I'll see you in the week.'

Well, fuck me, I ain't gone two hours when Kenny's on the phone: 'Mum, she's gone.'

'What, not again!'

Twenty minutes later the phone goes; it's her. 'I'm at the station, Joy, can I come over because the train's broke down.'

So she turns up; Wayne's asleep. I'm pretending I don't know, so I said, 'You had a row?' She said, 'No!' So I said, 'Come in the kitchen and I'll make you a cup of tea.'

'It's no good . . .'

'Now, Sharon, please stop coming over. This kills me to say this, it kills me because I want to see the baby, but I think you and Kenny are finished.'

'I feel as if I could scream . . . I don't have to put up with this!' She's a bombastic little bastard!

I said, 'At the moment your rent's being paid, your electric light's being paid, you haven't got no worries. You can sit down and smoke all day! If you leave where will you go? You ain't got no mum and dad. You'll end up in a furnished room. It's better that you bite your tongue and make a life.'

'Well, I can't!'

'Well then, don't! Because Kenny doesn't love you, but God give you this baby because you lost your mum and dad, and it will break my heart if I don't see the baby, but you've got to do what's best for him. And I mean it.'

So she said, 'Can I come over on Tuesday?'

She's going out as if she's got nothing to wear. The other day I bought her a beautiful long skirt – oatmeal, what you can wear boots with. She don't wear it; instead she puts this white powder on her face and this gel on her hair so it all sticks up in the air. Well, my Kenny doesn't like nothing like that. He said to her the other day, 'You had a scare, Sharon?'

She's twenty-two now and I done all her highlights for her. Anyway, she's having her hair cut, but then she wears these clonky shoes and she looks dreadful, I'm telling you. She says, 'He drinks, he gambles.' I said to him, 'It's terrible how you've come down.' He says, 'Mum, I do it because I won't go home!' My little Wayne looks at me, and I get hold of him and I whisper to him, 'Are you Joy's baby?' and I kiss him on his cheek. He turns his little head so his lips go on my mouth and Sharon says, 'I'm sure he knows you!' And he's only six weeks old. I cuddle him and I sing all different songs to him and she says, 'He definitely knows you, Joy,' and as soon as I put him down in my house he cries. He's beautiful.

Kenny come over to me and he said, 'Mum, help me or I'll kill her.'

'What are you going to kill her for?'

'Because she's so wicked and spiteful.'

So I rang Helpline and explained everything to them. They wanted to speak to Sharon, so I fetch her over my house and she told them that he beat her up, which was lies. I'm not going to say he never punched her, because he punched her in the arm and punched her in the back.

Well, you read about it happens to other people, but when it happens to you . . . Helpline offered her a place at Wallingford. I don't know how I found the way, but when we got there a young girl let us in. There were all prams stacked up in the hall. She never cry, but I burst out crying, couldn't believe it was happening to me. The other women said, 'Don't cry; are you her mother?'

'No, I'm her boyfriend's mother.' I said, 'Sharon, are you sure you want to stay here?'

Anyway, then the time comes for me to go and she definitely wants to stay so I have to say 'Goodbye' to Wayne. Well, I don't know how I found the way home. I bought a bottle of brandy and I drunk the lot. Every drop! It made me ill, the drinking and the crying, it made me ill all week. Anyway she came over the next day and she seemed all right.

My Kenny isn't a womaniser. I said to her, 'Think yourself

lucky, he could have been washed and dressed and you're stuck indoors, and you couldn't do nothing about it! Like they did years ago! Wayne's all right, but,' I said, 'you must keep him to a routine.' He's not my baby, and I've come to terms with that now and I always ask her if I can pick him up. Or I say, 'Give him to me so you can have five minutes' rest.' And then I give him a cuddle.

I should have seen the signals before he got involved with her. I kept pushing Kenny away and he is my son. It's my fault really. Then when things went wrong, I said to him, 'If you go back with Sharon, you'll end up killing each other.'

I said to Sharon, 'You think he'll be what you want him to be, but he won't be.'

I should never have let him go with her, I blame myself. He should never have got tied up with her; she's completely wrong for him. I mean that. He needs a girl that's full of life and that'll hold the reins on him. Every man needs to be pulled up, but cunningly. Take me and Big Don; he'd scream and shout and one thing and another, and to make that go I'd shut up quiet, but I'd do him in another way. I'd say, 'I've got to have this,' and 'I want this done,' and the more I made it more lovelier at home the less rows we had. With a man you've got to be very crafty; you've got to coax him, they're still like little boys really. If we coax them the right way, they look after us, and I try to explain this to Sharon, but she buys these picture books, these love stories, and she thinks everything should be different.

Kenny needs a person very like himself, someone who is strong, but not domineering. He is so like me – I can see myself in him – you be good to him and you can have the world, you aggravate him and he'll hate you. I did feel sorry for him yesterday, not because he's my son, but I did feel sorry for him. When she walked away, she's got the baby tied up in front of her, this fucking old blue coat on. I've given her a pram and she's not using it; she doesn't like this and she doesn't like that. I've got to start thinking about myself . . . and Wayne.

I never ever thought that this would end up like this. I always thought I'd have a grandchild and I could visit him and he'd come and stay with his nan. Really and truly, my whole world has been disillusioned because I've lived in fairyland. There is some people make it beautiful . . . He's a dear little soul and what I dread is him mixing with bullies in case he isn't tough. I want to make him secure. If she left him, I'd have him, I wouldn't put him away. I'd have him. I often think of this. I can't see her doing it, but then on the other hand I can.

I would like to say, 'Sharon, look in that mirror. We all have to sacrifice things when we have babies. You've got to smarten yourself up. Look at your hair. Now, go and get those reinforced pantyhose, and start holding your stomach in and wear proper brassieres so you have a good lift-up.' I said to her, 'Men go off you if you don't keep yourself nice! That's when they start looking for other women.' I only tell her for her own good. I said to her, 'You've got to pull yourself together and get yourself some clothes.'

I feel like this little baby's mine, when I'm on my own I do. I'd love to have been a mother again. Not the pain, I don't like that, but I'd love to have been a mother again. I think this is my Kenny again. They're feelings you can't explain. You're affected by your grandchild, I don't know what it is. I love him, I can't explain how much I love him. I've always wanted a grandchild. We're going fishing; we're going to Spain together. When I'm fifty-five, I'll get the holidays half-price and he can come and sleep in the same room as me. I'll make sure that baby's all right while I'm alive. As long as I can work and buy him something, he'll have it. I want to do everything for this baby that I never did for Kenny. I've always been a good mother, but I haven't been the best mother. He's never gone without, but with this baby I'd like him to be able to say when he's five or six, 'I've got the best grandmother.'

A YEAR LATER

The following year, on the same day of the same month, Wayne's birthday, Sharon gave birth to a daughter and Joy had a grand-daughter. She was named Carmel. Joy was in the waiting room at the hospital taking care of Wayne and held her in her arms just five minutes later.

When I go to see Wayne, I knock on the door and look throught the letterbox and I call him. As soon as he hears me, he runs to the door and as I go in he holds his arms in the air to be picked up. I was in a bit of a mood last Wednesday because Sharon was still in bed and it was one o'clock. She said she had been up all night. Little Carmel was in her basket and Wayne was in his pyjamas and I said to him, 'How's your little sister?' but he didn't want me to look at her, he wanted me to take him out straightaway.

So I changed his nappy and got him up, and I made a cup of tea. The talcum powder was all over the bathroom, the toys were everywhere, the washing-up was in the sink. I told myself to block it out and say nothing, so I ironed all Kenny's shirts and then I took Wayne for a walk holding his hand. The way he walks, he's fantastic, not because he's ours, he really is, he's only one year old and he'll walk miles.

Then I brought him home, and I washed up for her and hung the washing out, and then I played with him and Sharon said, 'I don't want you spoiling him because he screams when you go.' I hate leaving him now, that's why I like to go when he's not looking. He loves my bag and my lipsticks. He likes putting it on me and then he started to put it all over his own face, so now I have to hide the lipstick.

I've shown him how to stroke Carmel softly, but he pats her too hard, and then he got hold of her cardigan and nearly pulled her out of her basket, so I think he might be a little bit jealous. She's only six weeks old and her little face is really filling out, but her eyes are still very sad. I looked at her and I touched her and I bought her a new dress, which I must really stop buying, but I'm not really with her yet, I know it sounds cruel. I picked her up and I cuddled her. I made Sharon take all the washing to the laundrette and Wayne had gone to sleep, so there was just me and Carmel, and I wrapped her up and gave her her bottle, but she took too long to feed, she took ages, and I winded her and I looked at her. She is a dear little soul, a very dear little baby, but Wayne I am so taken with, perhaps because he reminds me of my Kenny and I was the first one to hold him, remember. When he came out I'll never, ever forget it; it was beautiful and I was there. I haven't clicked with Carmel yet. I love her, but it's coming slowly and I loved Wayne from the moment he was born. Carmel hasn't got any character yet, she just sleeps and eats and I haven't got used to her.

I told Sharon that Wayne is getting jealous. She's put him to sleep in the little room on his own and they have Carmel in with them. I told her, 'Put them in together, otherwise he's going to feel lonely.' And she says, 'No,' and of course I get the hump when she won't do what I tell her.

I just can't believe I've got two grandchildren. I'm only going once a week now. I'll go after work once a week and spend a few hours. I mustn't kill myself, they're not my children. To be truthful, I can't handle it at the moment, there's too much happening in my own life.

I love beautiful things and I'd love to make it all lovely for them. Sharon is a good mother, I've got to say that. I can't take that away from her. I've bought her so many clothes for the kids that even if she didn't do no washing for a fortnight she's got enough to last! I ironed so many little vests, and goodness knows what. I said to her, 'You're in bed when you should be up and out with the kids; it'll be bad enough in winter when you have to stay in.' She said, 'But I've got so much to do,' and I said, 'But you've got nothing to do here; you've got two children, they're your main problem. Once they're in bed of a night, then you clear up.' Nell, if you'd have walked in there the other day you would have run out. Fucking hell, I nearly died! I could fucking shake her. All she's got to pay is her electric light and her gas and the food. Kenny gives her a hundred pounds a week, and he gets the meat. She should be all right, fucking hell, babies don't eat that much. I've bought her clothes she never wears, she's so big. She slings everything on the floor, she don't hang nothing up.

Nell: Do you love Sharon?

Joy: Love Sharon? Of course I do. She's family, isn't she? Besides, she's the daughter I never had.

I've got a new love affair going. I feel a bit selfish, because I want all my time with Bill and there isn't enough minutes in the day. I want one afternoon a week with the kids, but I said to Bill, 'If I get married to you, they'll be your grandchildren as well.' He never answered. Then he said, 'I've got my children off my back and I don't want to have no more.' And I said, 'If you have me, you've got to have my grandchildren.' So he said, 'Well, you have your after-noons, love, and if you're tired when you come home I'll cook the dinner.' But I know I must tread lightly and not push too much on to Bill. If I make enough fuss of him he won't mind. They all love you if you give them plenty of fuss.

What I would honestly like would be a little house with a garden where they could come and stay with me for a weekend about once a month. I'd visit them every week and when they got older I'd take them to the zoo. I'd like her to be a ballet dancer and for him to play the guitar. I want to be a real grandmother and always to have time for them, but sometimes you can't be bothered.

CATO LEARNS TO GO DOWN STEPS

WHEN I HAVEN'T seen Cato for a couple of weeks I am longing to see him, but I enjoy the longing, whereas I hated being apart from my own children. When they went to their father's for a week I found the separation very painful. I don't find this with Cato. I think about him a lot, but I don't need to live with him. One full day a fortnight is right for me at the moment. I do nothing else on that day but have a bath and breakfast, and then I go and fetch him. We spend the day together and at night I take him home.

I feel if I have him once a week instead of once a fortnight, I'm not going to be able to cope with my life. What about my life as a writer? I'm not sure if this fear is some endless, frantic struggle with time and an urgency that I've always had and should now let go of, or if there is some reality. I don't really know. Yet there are things that I couldn't do without him, like spending a weekday afternoon with friends and babies in the sun rather than being at home working. He takes away the guilt; if he's on my knee, I'm not idle.

I have to remind myself that he won't die if he gets bored or cross or cries. There's still a bit of me that thinks, 'How disastrous!' Each time I have him I get more confident with him and he gets bolder. Last week I sat reading the paper while he crawled along the passage to the kitchen because May and Ivy were in there and he loves watching them. I had put a cushion at the bottom of the two steps going into the kitchen in case he fell and then I went on reading the paper in the sitting room. After about five minutes I heard this great shriek and ran out – he had tried to get down the steps and had got stuck halfway and panicked! He had not yet learnt to turn around, so he had one hand on the step below and his other arm stuck desperately up in the air. He was howling with fright. I picked him up and he clung to me and I was touched that he could find comfort in me. He sat on my knee and sucked his fingers, and after a while he wriggled to get down and start on his adventures again. This time I came too and helped him turn round when he got to the steps so he went down feet first. He was pleased and went up and down several times. I clapped and he clapped too.

After lunch he fell asleep and I listened to the radio. When he woke we went to the bank on the number 11 bus to Sloane Square. We both got quite excited about our bus ride. We get on at a request stop and the bus comes over a humpbacked bridge, so you only see its red roof when it's nearly upon you. It was a struggle to hold Cato in my arms and fold the pushchair at the same time, and then flag down the speedy bus and leap, no hands, on to the platform, carrying baby and pushchair, and pretending it was easy-peasy, and I did it every day.

He loves kneeling up on the seat just inside the door and looking out. Usually I sit upstairs in the front of the bus, pavement-side, but it would have been tricky carrying him up the stairs, so now we've got a little routine of inside on the bench seat, him kneeling, nose pressed to the window, me beside him. I'm so proud when he goes out with me. I tell everyone he's my grandson. One day we'll sit on the top at the front and go all the way to St Paul's Cathedral, me and my friend.

CHAPTER 5

Susie

SUSIE HAS TWO daughters: *Vivien, who is married to James, and has Lucy and Jessica; and Jane, who is married to Neil and has Sarah. Susie's husband, now dead, was a GP in London. She lives in an early-Victorian cottage in Fulham, with a street market at the end of the road. Everything in the house is individual and beautiful, yet simple. She has a collection of lustre jugs and mugs. In the garden at the front are hellebores, hostas, roses, clematis, viburnum and hydrangeas; in the back are tree peonies, hollyhocks, ceanothus, potentilla and pansies and birch trees.*

Susie works as a freelance organiser, a job description I have invented; she says she 'sorts people out'. In reality, when your practical life is upside down, Susie arrives, and the same day you find yourself in possession of new filing, a clean desk, black bags full of rubbish, a light heart and clear instructions on how to keep your new life running. At least, that's what happened to me.

Yesterday I bought an inflatable paddling pool. I haven't had a paddling pool for about twenty years and I thought, 'Goodness, they're still quite cheap; only seven pounds for all that fun!' Today, it was hot, so I blew up the pool and sat Cato and two little plastic boats in the shallow water. Later Susie came over with Jane and her two-year old granddaughter Sarah who, seeing the pool, immediately stripped off and joined Cato. Susie, the experienced grandmother, doesn't even attempt to have a conversation with me, this we'll do later when the babies are back at home, but we three

*are happy enough, sitting in the sun, watching the babies passing
each other boats. Time seems to stand still and I flit back to
other summers, other babies, picnics on the grass, peanut-butter
sandwiches and melted chocolate biscuits. I love being out of doors.
I love having this little boy near me.*

*Now Sarah and Cato have had enough. I run and fetch towels
from the bathroom, and we lift them out of the water and dry them
on our laps.*

My grandmothers

I never knew my paternal grandmother, but when I was ten,
my parents were divorced, and my mother, my sister and I
went to live in a cottage on land belonging to my maternal
grandmother and step-grandfather on Hayling Island. As a
result, I saw a lot of my grandmother, but she was never
very nice to me. Her name was Blanche and she was a
statuesque Welsh woman who became a medium. She called
herself Madame Voyez and had rooms by Liberty's depart-
ment store in London. She was the rage of post-graduates
from Oxford and Cambridge. She had a chaperon and did
her clairvoyancing with the chaperon there, and the young
men used to flock. It was a spooky time before the 1914 to
1918 war, ectoplasm and all that! They used to have table-
turning seances.

I guess she was intent on marrying for money. Although
I tried to find things out, grown-ups were very secretive in
those days. I couldn't get through this secretiveness and it
was through my getting to know Joan, my mother's younger
sister, that I learnt about Blanche's past. Eventually my
grandmother married a rich and interesting man soon after
my mother was born; this was my step-grandfather. He was
a nice man and it was his cottage we went to live in when
my father left.

Grandmother Blanche was obviously psychic. She foretold the sinking of the *Titanic*, watching her sail down the Solent on her maiden voyage; and cancelled reservations on the *Lusitania* for the voyage on which it was torpedoed, but was happy to accept in exchange, at great inconvenience to the family, tickets on its penultimate voyage to New York, sailing within twenty-four hours of my distraught but trusting grandfather cajoling the authorities to alter the booking and yet not being able to admit why the change was necessary.

My grandmother was mean to me. Like a lot of grandmothers she favoured her eldest grandchild, who was my sister. She was crabby and critical and put-downie and I can't remember that I ever had a conversation with her without fear that she was going to find fault with me. I got adept at avoiding her by running down the back stairs so I didn't have to go past the open door of her bedroom. She made cosmetics and bottles of various lotions and she had a house in the garden where she printed batiks. She was obviously a talented woman, but she never liked me. I used to walk about whistling, I loved whistling, but I had to stop because it 'hurt her ears'. My step-grandfather was frightened of spiders and she used to threaten him with spiders if he displeased her.

Eventually, I went to live with my aunt Joan who was on non-speaking terms with her parents. Joan became a sort of mother to me when I ran away from my mother. She was also psychic. I learnt from her that my mother was illegitimate and that my grandmother never let her forget this. I loved Joan to such an extent and became so overwhelmed with this wonderful woman that I spent every holiday with her, and she replaced my mother and my grandmother. She loved me and I loved her. She rescued me from my mother and I fell in love with her completely. I was besotted by her. She knew me very well and we had a lot in common. She was, I suppose, my salvation.

It's from when they're born right up to when they start school that you can be most useful; just to wade in and do that terrible pile of ironing. It's a tremendous pleasure ironing all those tiny vests and dresses, and then the baby's asleep so I gossip with my daughter. I didn't necessarily get it right. I feel guilty in some ways about not having given a day a week; perhaps I was hedging my bets that something wonderful might turn up and I'd have to turn it down. But when Lucy was born, Vivien didn't have any help so I was really there a lot. It was just a question of getting in the car and driving to Clapham and then doing whatever was necessary. I must say that, to begin with, I was terribly tentative about picking up this little bundle because I had completely forgotten what it was like. Viv was marvellously competent from the start and gazed with great friendliness at my attempts to be clever at handling this tiny baby.

As soon as Lucy was weaned I got one of those collapsible cloth cots and I had her for the odd night so that she got used to me. Then when Vivien was pregnant with Jessica she left Lucy with me for two weeks so they could have a holiday before the new baby was born. Lucy was only eighteen months old then and at first she was appalled, but only for one night, then she settled. I'd far rather they stayed with me than I moved into their house. When they were young and woke in the night I could never really get back to sleep again, so that when Vivien came back from holiday she said, 'My God, you look tired!'

Now that they're older it's absolute bliss when the little girls come to me. I just do whatever I want to do and they come along. Lucy, who is five, spends a lot of time making words on a travel Scrabble. I'll suggest a word and she'll find the letters. Up till two and a half they demand all your attention, but of course you're delighted to give it. You can do all those special things with the smalls that you wanted to do with your own children, but you also had to cook dinner and clean the house and make all the beds plus look after a husband, whereas if you have a baby for the day you can do whatever you want to do. There seems more time simply to enjoy the baby.

Now the children have a lot of friends and they go out to tea, I am tentative. Sometimes I wonder if I push myself a bit too much to the London ones, but actually I think that's just me being a bit pathetic. Lucy and Jessica run at me when I arrive which I love and Sarah is always standing on the doorstep waiting with a huge grin. You might feel this tentativeness more with a daughter–in–law than a daughter; in–laws can be a breeding ground for problems.

I supported my younger daughter Jane when she persuaded Neil to give the baby her bottle sometimes. He is besotted by Sarah now, but he was a bit worried to begin with, having never handled a baby before. Now he gets up on a Saturday or a Sunday and gives Sarah her breakfast. He's incredibly good at talking to her and playing with her. He's teaching her the guitar.

I hadn't had Sarah for a night on her own since she was eight months old, so when I was going to have her for the weekend I said to Jane, 'Bring her just before and stay too, so she can get used to the little cot again.' I love Jane bringing Sarah for a couple of days. Living in Aylesbury you can't just come up for a day because you're driving both ways in the rush hour, so it's a good excuse to have them for longer. Since Jane had Sarah our relationship has grown. There's much more common ground. Before this baby we'd go for weeks without seeing each other. Every now and again I think, 'Gosh, how noisy it is,' but then of course it's almost too quiet once they've gone.

I don't think Jane or Neil had much idea what a baby would do to their lives, or how a baby ticked. I saw both my daughters fall into the traps I did when I was first a mother, thinking, at six weeks old, that the baby is crying on purpose to annoy. But when you're a grandmother you see the amazing clear slate a baby is and that they're no more capable of being manipulative than adding two and two. I don't think I ever saw that as a mother.

Keep a diary when they stay with you. I kept a diary the first time Lucy came to stay with me for a fortnight as if she'd written it herself: 'Gosh, you left me in the lurch, but I couldn't have cared less by the next morning. Gully stroked my head and gave me Phenogen!' It entranced her mama. I think the children will love it when they grow up; people are obsessed by themselves and always want to know what they were like when they were children. They call me Gully. Lucy was trying to say 'Granny' and it came out 'Gully' and that has stuck and I like it.

Having my little granddaughters to stay is completely different from when my own daughters were children. My desire is just to lie on the floor and let them do whatever they want to do. Emotionally you can afford to fill them up and over with love. I'm very conscious now of coming down to a child's level and sitting or lying on the floor as opposed to hovering above them and giving orders, and I have a feeling that as a mother I was always above them and never actually sat down, or lay on the bed and played with them. Life was so busy! I expect I did sometimes.

In a funny way, when they're in my house I don't even need a box of toys, anything in the house will do. They love my japanned jewellery box – they put eighteen rings on each finger. They have a very self-important feeling about coming to my house: they come in as if they owned it and will look around to see if everything is as they left it last time. They check my belongings, like my fireplace full of stones. They are more interested in my things than the box of toys. And they never expect to take anything away with them. Lucy is particularly interested in animals, and she will go out into the garden and count the beetles under the pots and collect up all the slugs and snails.

We have conversations about potty training. I don't believe in rushing it. If you look round you, the majority of grown-ups we know are potty-trained – you don't have to worry much! Most babies if they are left to themselves are dry by two and a half anyway.

I worried a lot when Jane was depressed after Sarah was born, but I don't worry about the things that haven't happened yet. When she needed me I was going every other day, but I'd come home at night: it was only an hour and a bit. If it's necessary, you do cancel the rest of your life. I have an incredibly full diary, but all of it would be cancelled if either of my daughters wanted me for any important reason at all. I wonder if they know that? We do have clear and frank conversations sometimes, but not always. I remember about five years ago Vivien saying to me, 'If ever I say, "Come and live with us," I shall mean it, because I shall never say it if I don't mean it.' And I know this is true because she's devastatingly honest.

I don't thing there is anything I wouldn't tell either of them. Remember you're still a mother. Nobody stops being a mother until they become senile. Then the roles change. When your children are grown-up you don't do a lot of hugging and kissing unless something catastrophic happens, but I'm constantly rolling over the babies and kissing them – they are so huggable! You can act totally emotionally and innocently, cuddling the grandchildren.

I didn't expect all the pleasure, I just didn't expect it; I don't know why. My mother certainly didn't feel it. It is such a joy. The most satisfying thing is sitting on the floor with my daughter, uninterrupted, and watching the baby playing with a cardboard box. We play Peek-a-Boo with Sarah, who thinks she can't be seen, oblivious of the fact you can see all of her except her two eyes. Of course she is convinced that because she can't see you, you can't possibly see her – terrible giggles with your child about her child. I suppose it is an unspoken communion; it brings you closer together.

I've noticed the little girls always behave better with me than with their mothers. Jessica does this 'Lady Macbeth' act to Vivien – arms in air, 'distraite' face – and even when she is absolutely exhausted Vivien will pick her up. I would change the subject or sit down. I'm not an indulgent grandmother. I can be quite crisp. I'm very seldom noisy cross, but they know what makes me cross – like emptying a drawer on to the floor or throwing something. I've never smacked them and I'm a smacker. I'd only smack them if they made me very angry, like crossing the road when I'd told them not to. Once Jessica took a favourite mug and hurled it on the hardest bit of the floor she could find. I was furious, but I didn't smack her because she was only two and didn't know what she was doing. But I *was* furious and she howled. I have a feeling that if I smacked either of them they would be appalled, because I'm sure mothers can smack with impunity, but not grandmothers.

I didn't love my mother or my grandmother when I was a child. I think I loved my father, but he disappeared when I was young so that wasn't much good. I didn't love my sister either, so really I grew up very short of loving till Joan came into my life.

I've gone on spending money on the children when I've wanted to. I nearly always arrive with a basket of things, sometimes things I've come across in my own house. I don't so much bring presents for the children, otherwise they may look forward to the present rather than seeing you! I will not buy them sweets. Lucy came with some pocket money the other day and she said, 'I think I might buy some sweets.' I said 'No, not while I'm around; you can do that with your mother.' 'Why can't I buy sweets, Gully?' 'I don't like it.' And that was fine.

I've never stopped myself spending money on them. You see something and if you've got the money, you buy it! And just remember if you're ever in Paris, the children's clothes are miles smaller because French children are midgets compared to English children. Sarah hadn't got anywhere to put her dresses, so I went to Peter Jones and bought a lovely little cupboard with three drawers and a hanging rail and I put it in my car. It just fitted, with me bending over the steering wheel and not being able to change gear, but when I got to Jane's they were thrilled and so was I. It was a ridiculously dangerous journey.

I don't know how my relationships with my three little granddaughters will develop. I know exactly where I am with Sarah, she is only eighteen months old, but with Lucy, who is five and a half, and Jessica, who is nearly four it's different. I respond to their demands and I don't dictate anything, but I just don't know how I'll respond as they get older. I think I'll react to what they are rather than think back to what they were.

I've got a friend who's a grandmother – I think she's a much better grandmother than I am – and sometimes we get together and have tea. I took Sarah to tea there and Jane came too, and her daughter has a baby the same age. We all sat on the floor and watched the babies and gossiped.

ANOTHER AFTERNOON A FEW MONTHS LATER

Sometimes I feel guilty about not taking Sarah more often to help out Janey, but it's this 'out of London' business, although in fact I do go to Aylesbury once a week. Then I think, 'I wonder if Vivien minds?' but of course I go to her at the drop of a hat for a couple of hours because it's only ten minutes away. You're always wondering if you do more for one than for the other. I realise there's a lot of self-gratification in my visiting and the point is it's going to stop: the children will go to school when they're three or four, so I've only got a few years. This day a week or day a fortnight is precious.

The first time Vivien and James went skiing, I stayed in their house to look after Lucy and Jessica and, apart from the fact that they woke in the night and would come pattering down and get into my bed and I'd never have another wink of sleep, it was a good time. It was also sometimes the 'yawning boredom' of trying to amuse one or two small people for four hours. I'd look at my watch – they'd had their rest and it was another three hours till bedtime. When I was in Vivien's house I didn't have anything to do; you can't start cleaning the silver in someone else's house.

One afternoon when I was there, I made them a house with rugs and cushions over the table. They took one brief look at it and asked for something else, and despair swept over me and I thought, I'm never going to 'amuse' these children again, I've taken the wrong tack. So now when they come to my house, I do what I want to do and I've stopped amusing them. And they love it. When I garden, they turn over pots for the worms and the woodlice, and they're out of doors and they're helping and watering. Or I'll tidy out a cupboard with them, or do the ironing while they draw. I'm sure the secret is that you do your own thing at home, and they join in.

When I go to Jane's, we take care of Sarah together and Jane says, 'It's such fun when you're here,' as we watch Sarah climb in and out of a laundry basket. If you're on your own you don't have that collusion and it's boring hour after hour. The time goes so quickly if we're there together. Sarah's getting old enough to object to our endless conversations, so she starts to sing and you can't say, 'Shut up!' to a child who's singing because she's being creative! Lucy and Jessica did just the same when Vivien and I gossiped for too long; they'd both sing.

I'm profoundly affected by the responsibility: the number of times when I remember with horror I've left the sleeping pills beside my bed. None of my cupboards with such things as bleach and so on are childproof. Yesterday I found half a needle embedded in my hair-cord carpet upstairs and I'd had Sarah for two nights! I don't know how it got there.

Sarah once did this appalling thing of swallowing a penny when she was with me. Jane was there too. I had a pig with lots of pennies in it and suddenly Sarah started to choke. I knew straightaway that it was a penny. She was eighteen months old. Jane banged her on the back, but she went on choking and Jane panicked: 'Mummy, what shall we do? What shall we do?' I was in a panic too – this had never happened to me before. I held her upside down by her heels and put my finger down her throat, whereupon all her tea came up plus the penny!

You see, having been married to a doctor is very bad training. In an emergency with my own children I went to him, so I can give endless medical advice to people, but give me a good panic and I'm lost. My mother was paranoid about danger – teddy bears weren't allowed to have eyes – but you can't make it absolutely safe. I just take some precautions, like putting the sleeping pills away; I've also got plug covers. You have to keep an eye on the children: when they're crawling, they move so quickly. I put a gate at the bottom of the stairs and, after Lucy fell down the step in my kitchen and cut her lip, I put cushions there. You've got to let them find out about danger so they can begin to look after themselves, but you've got to guard against serious harm. You have to cast your mind back to how you pro-tected your own children.

My relationship with each of my three grandchildren is

different. Perhaps there's an aspect of me that one of them responds to in a different way from another.

When the third grandchild came along, Janey's first and probably last, the anxiety about the birth was the same, although Jane and Neil were cleverer and didn't tell me till it was all over. My initial interest was in responding to Janey's need and dealing with it, before unwrapping this new and unknown parcel: I think a daughter would always take precedence over a grandchild, but possibly not a daughter-in-law. I don't know what I'd have been like if my grandchildren had been my daughters-in-law's and not my daughters'. I suppose you can take a lot for granted with your own children, you can say what you like. I'd advise a grand-mother to find out what baby book her daughter or daughter-in-law is using and buy the same book. Vivien has Penelope Leach and I got one for Jane which I read when I'm there.

The birth of my first grandchild was awful for me, sitting there sewing bloody cushions and ringing the hospital and saying, 'Will you tell my son-in-law he can come back and sew the cushions, and I'll go and sit with my daughter.' It was absolutely awful: my child was in pain and she was frightened. She was late, so they took her into hospital. Labour lasted all that evening and the following morning, although it seemed much longer than it actually was. Then James rang and told me the baby had arrived. I was choking, I wanted to burst into tears! I went to the hospital; I remember walking into a room at Thomas's and my first look was for Vivien – I always know if she's all right at the first glance – then I looked at the baby. She was in her little hospital crib and was very, very beautiful. I couldn't believe how small she was. She was extraordinary – everybody could see she was beautiful!

CHAPTER 6

Joan

JOAN LIVES IN a little village in Antigua. Her house is made of wood and sits up on stilts with a balcony at the front. The rooms are divided by wooden screens with open fretwork along the tops. The garden has mangoes and coconut palms and goats and chickens. The shower is rainwater warmed by the sun. Her dogs, Pudding, Charlie and Number Three, sleep under the house. Her daughter Kim and son-in-law Winston live opposite with Sunny, their four-year-old daughter.

Joy took me to stay with Joan in Antigua in February. We slept in a double bed under a mosquito net in a little room next to her. We could talk to each other at night, our voices drifting back and forth over the wooden partition. In the morning Joan woke first and made us all tea, and brought it in and sat on our bed with a big tin of biscuits, singing along to the local radio station. Sunny skips into the room, golden-skinned and dark-eyed with black hair, slender as a salamander in her crisp white dress, and suddenly stops dead, shy at finding strangers there. She has come to say 'Good morning' to her grandmother on her way to school.

Each morning, Joy and I strolled through the garden to Juba's shop, which was a small wooden hut with a green tin roof, to buy bread for breakfast. Sometimes we had an ice-cold beer from the fridge at eight o'clock in the morning, sitting on bar stools with contraceptives called Rough Riders festooned in bundles over our heads and little boys playing cricket on the smooth grass just outside the door. Little girls strolled about in immaculate lacy frocks, holding hands with baby brothers and sisters, their hair done up in fancy ways. Juba was a transvestite and wore a different dress every day, each one more wonderful than the last. His shop sold nearly everything that anyone could possibly want: pink and green hairnets, high-heeled plastic shoes with little flowers on the toes, sweet potatoes, bananas, semolina. Most customers stopped a while to talk. It began to get hot, too hot to hurry home. Joy and I had another beer.

In the afternoons we'd go down to the beach with Joan and Sunny, and dream about how next year we'd bring our own little grandchildren, Cato and Wayne. At night we went dancing and came home at three in the morning, carrying our shoes, and crawling under the mosquito net with great difficulty, glad that we hadn't brought Cato and Wayne with us.

My Grandmothers

I was born in 1933 at home in London, in the house next door to my father's parents. I was nearly three months early and that was before incubators. The doctor told my mum I wouldn't survive, but she wrapped me in cottonwool and kept me in bed with her and I did!

I can't remember much before I was about six or seven, but after that my memories down there are lovely. My parents moved to the other end of Putney near the High Street and as a kid I used to walk down to Pentlow Street where my father's parents and my aunt lived. It was like walking in the country. There were a lot of horses and carts, the milkman had a horse and cart. Poppins the grocery shop was a horse-and-cart delivery. I used to think that it was miles and miles to my grandparents, but now you couldn't let a child walk all that way, you'd be frightened for their safety. How many kids do you see playing on the streets these days? The key was on a piece of string in the letterbox. In the summer my grandmother sat outside on a chair in the front. She used to do her peas there on the doorstep. All the neighbours would be sitting outside when they weren't doing their odds and sods. They knew each other very well. At Christmas the piano would be wheeled out into the street and played, and everyone would sing.

I was a proper tomboy and the Thames was my playground. I couldn't swim, but there used to be logs floating in the river and we used to ride on them. I've had more caning from that than from anything. People used to tell my mum, 'I've just seen your Joan down on the river.' My mum used to dress me up in Shirley Temple dresses, and I used to take my dress off and leave it on the bank and play in the water in my knickers. They bought me a trike with pump-up tyres and mudguards; I loved it. I'd go down the street with half-a-dozen kids hanging on. There were orchards from Pentlow Street down across Beverley Brook stretching to the towpath.

My grandmother was always quite an old lady in a long dress and a pinny. I used to go and get her her Guinness. She'd put a hot poker in it to take the chill off and to put a bit of iron into it. I used to get it in a jug and I'd get a boiled sweet, I never got money. I used to run lots of errands for her and I'd help with the washing or feeding the chickens or getting dinner. I had an aunt who lived upstairs who I got on very well with, so I often used to sleep there with my cousin. It was my second home really. I loved the garden: it was a long garden with a shady place they made out of a canvas awning. There was a lilac tree and some deckchairs, and they'd take their tea outside in the summer. The chickens were at the end in a shed with a little run in front. My grandfather made me a cart and I had to fetch the chicken-meal on it. My gran would cook all the scraps and the potato peelings and I'd feed them to the chickens.

My gran didn't do a lot of kissing and cuddling like I do with Sunny, but she had a lot of grandchildren, so perhaps she didn't have the time to get to know them all well. If I went down there, it was mostly to play. If I ran errands for her, I would get a piece of toast and marmalade or a boiled sweet, but there was no show of affection. I can remember going once on a Sunday all dressed up in my Sunday-school clothes and she said, 'Your mother keeps you nice.' I can always remember her saying that, but other than that I never heard her praise me. She had a shelter built in the garden when we came back from Bedfordshire: a bomb had dropped on the Black and White milk bar in Putney High Street, and my gran was frightened and shouted to my aunt, 'Quick, get the gin bottle!' Her hand was shaking as she poured out the gin.

At the back of the street there were fields and we were encouraged to play out all day. Kids indoors were thought to be a bit of a nuisance, so if you weren't running an errand you made yourself scarce. I never sat and talked to my gran, but sometimes I cleaned her brass in the front room. I never remember anyone talking to me about school, or encouraging me, or taking an interest in me. I never remember my gran or my mum ever reading to me. You were really just part of what was going on. I don't remember anyone then saying they were short of money. There were always eggs and we picked mushrooms and nobody seemed to worry about too far ahead. There was a lot going on, so you were never bored.

My grandmother died when I was sixteen, a natural death of old age. All the family were with her; she had five sons. But I went dancing; my mum said that was the best thing to do as I was a bit young for a death-bed.

My mother's mother lived in Fulham in a flat, so I didn't see her so much. I used to walk over there with my mum sometimes. I was the eldest, so I would walk and she would push the two others in the pram. We'd go up Hurlingham and all along the back streets. That grandmother was tall, slender and dark; I think she was a bit of a gypsy. I never liked going there so much, because it was a flat and we'd sit and look at the photos and it was a bit boring because I was a tomboy. On the way home my mum would let me sit on the pram when I wasn't too heavy. It was a long walk, but we went every week.

MY GRANDDAUGHTER SUNNY

I see Sunny every day. I'm a real nanny, I get paid for looking after her. My daughter Kim said, 'Come to Antigua and look after Sunny, and I'll give you a wage.' She has married an Antiguan called Winston, and she started a pottery and supplies her home-made pots to all the hotels, as well as selling to the tourists, so she works full-time. I've looked after Sunny since she was six months old and now she's three and a half. Before that I was working on the riverboats. I've lived in London all my life and spent a good part of it working on the river.

I look after Sunny every day, but weekends I have off; I do need a rest from her now and again! She's started school now and she comes home at two o'clock. But it's not just working hours. My house is opposite Kim and Winston's and she'll come over at six o'clock in the morning while I'm still sleeping after a hangover. She'll stay till she's ready to go to school, and if she's brave enough I'll give her a cold shower and she'll have breakfast with me, then off to school she'll go.

When Kim came over here and then got married to Winston, I had no intention of coming over except for a holiday. First she told me she was going out with an Antiguan and then she fell in love with him. And really fell in love. I've never told my kids what to do. They do what they like, it's their lives. So she moved over here and set up her pottery. The pottery's caught on: she don't just sell to locals and tourists, every hotel in Antigua has her work, and thank God she's doing well, otherwise I'd have to go back to England. At first I had a little difficulty fitting in because I couldn't understand the Antiguans when they started talking. They all speak English, but a lot of them speak a rapid half-word talk. Now I tell them to slow up a bit; but many Antiguans are very educated.

I've had a lot of pleasure with Sunny. Really and truly, I've had more pleasure with Sunny than I had with my own two children because when I was young I was rushing here and there and working all the time. This time I've joined in with everything she's done. It's so different. How many times at home do you take your children to the beach? I used to take Kim to work with me. If she was tired, I'd give her a bottle and that was it; she'd have to sleep while I was working. Then later, from when they were quite small, I had to go to work full-time, and they were both in a nursery and after that it was school. Then when you came home you gave them their tea, played with them for a little while and then it was their bedtime.

I've had more pleasure in the playing with Sunny. I'm in the country here, whereas I was in a flat in London, looking at chimneypots and going to work. Here it's a different life for kids. They go to school early and they finish early and they spend the rest of their time outdoors. Sunny's got a tree house; my kids never had a tree house, they had a playpen in my kitchen. I didn't have anything, no money. When Sunny was small I used to push her down to the beach in the pushchair. Sometimes my friend Kay, she's Irish and Sunny's godmother, would come. We'd look like a gypsy caravan going down the road. We'd have everything, her dinner, her tea, her nappies, her bottle, and we'd spend the complete day on the beach with her. We'd take her swing down and hang it on a tree. She'd come in the water with us with her wings when she was six months old. I love her to death. With my own kids it's a different kind of love. From that time I saw Sunny, it was something that hit my stomach. I don't know whether it's because she's the daughter of my daughter.

I bet you every grandmother will say it's different. You have more time for them. I've had all my fun galavanting, running about here and there, trying to make a life. When I was young I wanted to leave my kids behind when I went out. Now, being a nanny, when she goes home to Kim I can go out. With my own kids I could never go out without them. During the day I was working and I couldn't afford a baby-sitter so I didn't go out.

When my husband fell in with another woman and left me, I felt that I was mother and father. I also felt I wasn't sharing my kids like I should have done. Even at Christmas I was doing it on my own. When he left, I rejected them for a while. I felt very depressed – my heart was too broken. In the end I came to terms with it. I realised he wasn't coming back and the three of us had better start a new life together. But Kim's life wasn't like Sunny's. Kim was like the little mother. She coped with a lot. Sometimes when I went to work on the boats I didn't know when I was coming home, and by the time she was eleven she was cooking all the dinners and she looked after Grant who was three years younger. Sunny's having a different life. People's children over here mean a lot to them; there are always parties. For birthday parties, you don't just have a couple of kids in, you have nearly half the island!

Sometimes I want to throw her back across the road because she has so much energy. Kim's a vegetarian, but over here Sunny gets spaghetti Bolognese and she loves that.

[77]

She's got to make up her own mind about what she likes, hasn't she? She loves to have a shower with me. I haven't got hot water, but the sun warms the cistern so it's not really cold. She loves to wash her hair, and then she insists on washing mine and I have to sit down on the floor of the shower so she can reach. You don't know what I do to keep her quiet. We have fun, me and her. She doesn't think of me as her nan, but as her little playmate.

Every Friday I buy her a book in the Ladybird series. She likes a little snuggle-up while I read to her. Sometimes she reads to me and I say, 'Here, who's reading this book, me or you?' When she cops the needle she's got a terrible temper. I might be helping her to colour a book and she doesn't like the colour I used, and she'll grab my pencil and throw it up in the air! And I'll say, 'Well, do it yourself!' and if she goes on being naughty I'll threaten her with the wooden spoon. If she's really bad I give her a smack and send her home. They've got to learn right from wrong. I've sent her home screaming her head off a couple of times. Five minutes later she's back, 'I do love you, Nan!'

She likes to cook and I let her scramble eggs. She makes a terrible mess, but I clear up after she's gone home. It doesn't bother me that I haven't got much money to spend on her. She has what I can give her. If I come in with a book she says, 'Oh that is beautiful!' She loves *Cinderella*, that's her favourite. If we're lying in bed together and I want to get her off to sleep so I can have five minutes' peace, I'll make a story up and that will send her off to sleep. She likes to stay the night with me. Sometimes I end up on the floor because she takes up all the room. She don't stop moving all night. She's a real fidgety-arse.

I'd like to live long enough to see her grow up. My mum saw a lot of my kids, we all grew up on top of each other. We were a typical Putney family. We never had any money, but we spent a lot of time together. Kim and I and Sunny often go to the beach together when she's finished work, or I'll be down on the beach with Sunny, and Kim will come down with some tea and we always have a laugh. She wants the pleasure of bringing her up as well.

My life here is Sunny, although I've got a good social life. I go dancing in the evenings. My friend Kay runs a bar and I can go up there and have a drink and a dance; if it's a Wednesday she's open till three o'clock in the morning and I come home with sore feet, carrying my clothes. Well, I couldn't do that in London!

She loves to make a pancake, Sunny! Somebody bought her a mixing machine. I said to Kim, 'You keep that in your house; it makes too much mess over here making pancakes.' Sometimes I get fed up because she's no angel, she's a tomboy. I have to climb the tree and sit up there with her. How many grandmothers climb trees? And it's a job to get up that tree, my size! I'd never done it, not since I was a little girl, I never climbed trees with my two kids. I never had time for a start, and I didn't have a garden and the only water my kids had was the sink.

She wants me to tell her stories and she's always talking to me. The only thing I mustn't say is 'bloody'. I do have a habit of saying 'Bloody dogs' when they've knocked over my dustbin, and the next moment she'll say, 'Look at those bloody dogs, Nan!' I've got to stop it. Kim told me I've got to stop swearing and I told her it comes out accidentally. I might say, 'Pick up those bloody toys!' Sunny says, 'You mustn't say "bloody",' so I say, 'Sorry, Sunny!' This has been one of the best times of my life, because she's captured for me the things I lost in my two kids from not being able to stop at home with them.

Winston is very good to Kim. When she had her friends and their children from England out to stay, Kim and Winston gave their bed up to them and Winston didn't care. He's a very kind man. She's got some lovely friends here.

Kim loves animals and that was awkward in London; over here she's had as many as six dogs at once.

My friend Kay used to live on a little island near Antigua called Barbuda and sometimes I took Sunny to stay with her. I'd say to Kim, 'Pack her bag; we're going to Barbuda for a few days.' The first time we went she was about one and a half. She loves the little six-seater planes. Kay was running a small hotel. It's so open and primitive there. As you opened the bedroom door you were almost in the sea; sand running into shallow water and masses of coconut palms and cottonwood trees. Kay had two tame goats that Sunny used to feed. They were her playmates and as long as she had her wings on she did what she liked. There was no electricity so the moon was our light at night; when it got too dark we all went to bed. There is only one tiny village and a couple of hundred people on the island. We had two bikes and we'd take her on the handlebars. It was all open bush and the roads were sand. She loved it, loved every minute of it. We'd collect coconuts or go into the village and see the little pigs. Once we got a lift on a coconut lorry; it was full of coconuts and we were in the back hanging on. We had a lot of fun with her.

A boat would come over every week bringing tourists and we'd put a notice on Sunny's back saying, 'Come to the Cockleshell for lunch.' Kay would bike down to meet the boat and ride around with Sunny on the back of the bike; we got lots of customers that way. Kay would cook fresh fish and spareribs and a lot of the locals would come up. She earned plenty of money on those days.

It's laid-back country here, you can't rush around. There are no trains, a couple of buses now and then. You don't worry about time; when it starts getting dark, just after six, you start thinking about cooking dinner, otherwise you go through the day at your own pace. They are very fond of their children here, but if the little boys are naughty they will give them a good smack because they think they are knocking the devil out of them.

Sometimes when I've got a bit of a hangover and I've got to keep my eye on her and climb trees when I'm not in the mood, then it's hard work. She wants to help me in everything I do. I daren't pick up a broom or a mop because she wants to do it. The broom's too big for her and it swings round and knocks something over and the water from the mop goes everywhere: it's easier not to try to do any work till she goes home. It's hard work, too, when it's very hot and she wants all kind of things, like having her dinner up in her tree house and she nicked my mustard. She took her porridge up the tree and sneaked the mustard out. Sometimes she sneaks my lipstick out, she loves dressing up. If anyone comes with high-heeled shoes she wants to try them on – she's ever so good at walking in high heels. When it's my weekend off and Kim wants to go to church, then I have her. At times I feel like having a lie-in and if she gets into that whiny mood it drives me nuts.

Once when we were on the beach she wanted to go to the toilet, so I took her along to the hotel toilets by the swimming pool and I left Kay on the beach. When she had finished I said, 'Now let Nanny have a tiddle and you go back to Goddy,' that's what she calls Kay, she's her godmother. When I got back to the beach I couldn't see her and I said, 'Is Sunny here?' and Kay said 'No.' I ran to the hotel pool and cor blimey if I didn't see her little bum floating in the water! She was under the water, but I knew it was her from the swimsuit, so I shouted, and a man walking past saw her and jumped in and pulled her out. She couldn't have been in more than a moment, because when we turned her upside down and hit her back she started to cough and choke and she was soon all right. She must have forgotten she'd taken her wings off to go to the toilet. Well, that's the sort of thing you've got to watch. It did frighten her and me! I had to tell Kim what happened, it shook us both up. When it comes to it, it's the responsibility that's hard. It's a very responsible job when you think of it, being a grandmother.

CATO IS ILL

WHEN I FETCHED Cato on Wednesday, perhaps because I was depressed, I wasn't quite ready for the physical hard work. To start with, there is lifting him in and out of the back seat of a two-door car, which is an acrobatic feat in itself: I hold him in my arms while I crouch in the tiny space behind the front seat and strap him into his chair. May and Ivy are in the back and the four of us make for Richmond Park through the drizzle. He is wearing cotton dungarees and socks and slippers and, although he has a warm coat and hat, I am worried he isn't dressed for crawling about on wet grass. But this morning he shows no desire to get out of his push-chair. The rain has stopped and the sky is a pale watery grey. The trees, heavy with leaves, drip on our heads as we go through the wood and I let the dogs run off into the thicket while we stick to the paths and have a calm walk.

When we get home nothing much seems to interest him and I feel bored, suddenly quite overwhelmingly bored by child care. Getting out the bricks, I build a castle; he doesn't clap, but tetchily knocks it over. It is too early to make lunch so I sit dully on the sofa feeling rather trapped. We are like a couple who have been married too long and find themselves alone at a seaside boarding house – nothing to do. He toys with his spaghetti Bolognese, but knocks most of it off the proffered spoon on to the floor for the dogs to lick up. Later we fetch Sharon and Wayne and go to the Drop-In Centre to cheer ourselves up, but Cato only plays fitfully, returning every few minutes to sit on my knee and lean his head against my arm, while Wayne races around. I still haven't guessed that he is ill, rather that it is my dreary mood that is causing his dreary mood.

We come back to my house for tea and Joy turns up. We are both happy to see our little grandsons together, but Cato doesn't want to eat or sleep or play, and at last I realise he isn't feeling well. I take him home and Nina his other grandmother is waiting for him. She is going to baby-sit tonight; his parents have gone out. We search for a thermometer and find a very modern-looking one with a digital window and a little button beside it. Neither of us knows how to work it. We try to take Cato's temperature, first under his arm which comes out at 77, then under his leg which comes out at 92; and then against his forehead which doesn't register at all. We can't find an old-fashioned thermometer. Then we try it on ourselves, me in my mouth and Nina under her arm (in that order), but can make no sense of it. The two grandmothers are disconcerted, the parents haven't left the telephone number of where they are. Should we ring the doctor? We find two baby books which recommend putting him to bed in a cool room with just a sheet over him and giving him water to drink. We do this and then I leave Nina to it.

I meet Cherry and we go to the cinema, and I realise I am not wiped out by Cato being ill as I was by my own children's illnesses, when I would have been incapable of going to the cinema even if someone else was looking after them, I would have been incapable of enjoying the film, so caught up would I have been in their temperatures . . . I think about Cato as I go to sleep, and ring early the next morning to hear that he has cut a big tooth and is fine.

CHAPTER 7

Ursula

URSULA LIVES IN the country by the sea. Her career was in all
forms of social problems; now retired, she sits on the Social Security
tribunals. Her other interests are music and all kinds of people,
which include her family. She is married to Robert and they have
three children: Helen, married to David and mother of Vera,
Magdalen, Gemma and Dorothy; a second daughter, Margaret;
and a son, John, married to Lucy, soon to have their first child.
(They have since had a baby daughter named Iona.)

Ursula took me to visit Helen's four little girls. They had been
for a walk in the rain and came in shaking their wet hair and
running barefoot about the house like bright fireflies here and there,
alighting for a moment on their grandfather's or grandmother's knee
and then off again to see what was going on elsewhere. There was
an ease between them all. When we sat around the kitchen table
for a cup of tea, Dorothy, who was only a year old, sat large-eyed
in her high chair gazing quietly out at the goings-on, and I thought
about what Ursula had said about Vera being a thinker and that
perhaps Dorothy would be a thinker too, and how lovely these four
little girls are, each one so different from the other, and how free
they are, nothing is forced upon them.

I coerced my children into behaving too well around grown-ups
and it was always a strain. Now family life, at its best, has become
more democratic. The strict parent has almost been abolished, and
parents and therefore grandparents don't expect children to behave

[85]

so well. In spite of what Ursula says about manners and discipline, I know she would agree; we are easier with them and everyone has a nicer time.

MY GRANDMOTHERS

I never knew my father's mother; she died before I was born. I can see from her photographs that she was very stiff. Both these grandparents were very Victorian and, by the look of their mouths, very buttoned up. I don't know if I would have taken to them as a child. They died long before I was born and nobody seems to have had any clear memories of them. I think they were rather deeply religious, but nobody's really passed anything down.

I knew my maternal grandmother well. We lived quite close, so on our way home from school, every day my sister and I always went in. She lived on a long road on the outskirts of the town, and from the ages of about ten and eight, we were allowed to take a tram and then walk up this road. We were both very fond of her. The house was dark inside: there were deep-blue velvet curtains and deep-blue upholstery, everything was dark, and there were no photographs. We would go straight in. My grandmother and her sister and my grandfather would be sitting there and we would say, 'We learnt this tune at school today,' and we'd sing it, and then my grandmother would sit down at the piano and play it. She could play any tune, and she sang to her playing and we loved it. We learnt all sorts of old songs and acted them out. She had a very large sofa, and we would get behind it and then dash out and either recite or act.

She and my aunt, who had a marvellous contralto voice and was a professional singer, would be endlessly sewing, mostly those collars they wore round their necks with the little bones to keep them stiff, which is why they always looked so upright. My aunt had a very long neck and she embroidered her collars. They always wore their necks covered and now that I'm getting older I think it's rather a good idea.

We always called my grandmother Gaggy; I don't know why. We never stayed the night. It was dark upstairs and she had endless pictures of battles with disembowelled horses, always a violent scene of battle. It was quite unlike her, because she was such a gentle person. They were frightening to us children; sometimes we'd walk upstairs and look at them and think how dreadful it was and we'd cry. We used to stay about an hour and then walk the mile and a half home for tea.

She was devoted to her son Alfred and she loved him much more than my mother. I remember noticing that as a child, but my mother was always very good to her and when the war started and I was fifteen, my grandparents and my aunt came to live with us.

I never felt I could tell my mother or my grandmother my problems. It was always my sister and I who talked about things. I admired my mother, but I don't remember loving her. I never remember throwing my arms around her with happiness, as I saw my little granddaughter greet her mother when we'd been out today. I never remember doing that. It just wasn't what you did, show that emotion. When I look back on it I think we were very subdued. We played in the garden a lot to keep out of the way. I remember having a closer relationship with the old gardener than anybody else; I was terribly upset when he died.

My grandchildren

Helen had had an infection and had been told by two Harley Street specialists that she couldn't have children. She came to grips with this when she was engaged. She had to tell David about it and we held our breaths, because we thought it might be the end of the engagement, but it wasn't. I realise now that that was due to David's stalwartness, which has been proved all the way through, whatever's happened, even though he is very highly strung. When I heard that she was pregnant my first feelings were of anxiety: was the baby going to be all right, was she going to be all right? When the baby arrived and she was fine, there was such an immense feeling of elation, and of course I made a tremendous number of resolutions because the baby had been allowed to come. I was perhaps over-emotional and was saying things like, 'I'll never tell another lie,' because I was so absolutely thrilled that it should have happened.

I couldn't go and see her because I had a cold, so I sent my sister who is very reactionary and said it was the most appalling hospital and I must take her out at once, which wasn't awfully helpful. I then saw her about a week later and it was an extraordinary moment, because I realised that in some, perhaps selfish, way, I thought this little girl was our future too: I immediately felt she was part of our family, that I was a factor in her life and that she was a factor in mine.

I didn't really get alongside the baby for a while because Helen had a maternity nurse and I felt that I was only allowed to see the baby on certain occasions at certain times. I remember feeling very much a stranger at that time because I wasn't allowed to go in and out, and I missed that. I was so thankful when the nurse went. Then I really could get alongside.

Helen didn't know a lot about babies and, after all, neither did I. That came to me very forcefully much later when Vera was eight months old and I learnt a very tough lesson. She was whingeing and I said, 'I don't think she has enough sleep for an eight-month-old baby.' Helen looked at me and said, 'Do you really know, Mum?' And I said, 'No, I don't really know,' because I didn't know with my own children. I really didn't know because we had had a nanny all the way through and I didn't know the routine, and I felt suddenly terribly useless because I was, just like she was, having to start from basics and I hadn't got any experience to fall back on that I could offer her. I felt that that was a terrible thing and that I had let her down dreadfully, because the grandmother is meant to be the fount of wisdom. I felt very sad about that. So we learnt together.

Helen and I have always been very close. Her having Vera was another dimension to the original relationship that we had. We definitely became closer because we had a shared experience of the baby, that marvellous thing, but it didn't make a sensational difference. She has always been very articulate about what was what and it made me realise I must be very careful about what I said, not because of the relationship but because I didn't really know, so I must always put my opinion in a tentative way to Helen. I would think, looking at a situation, that if it were me, I would do this, or I would not do this, but I could never speak with any authority. I think a lot of my generation are like that and some of their children understand it. You have to be very careful, because you have a lot of influence if you're close to your daughter, and you must be careful not to sow seeds that might not be based on anything other than instinct.

When the second baby was expected, because all had gone well with the first, I had much more confidence and really enjoyed it a great deal more, and she was a very different kind of baby. Magdalen was a tremendously outgoing baby, whereas Vera had been introspective from the very beginning, and still is now that she's eight. Since then Helen has had two more little girls, Gemma and Dorothy. She talks a lot to the children. She's always been a chatterbox so I thought it was just part of her make-up that she did, but they do talk all the time and I love that chatter.

[89]

Now that there are four little girls, I try hard to give Vera individual attention partly because she's the eldest. We do special things with her so that she feels that she's got her own entity, because everyone falls for Magdalen, the second one, because she's so friendly and pretty. I feel much more protective about Vera. I think a lot about her and of ways that we can build up her self-confidence. She's a tremendous bookworm, but that's partly an escape. She doesn't always read her book, but she takes it into her corner. I think that she's not that keen on human contact because she's not that sure of herself, and I want to help her to communicate more. Magdalen never has any problem at all; she is genuinely interested in people. Yet it's very strange with Vera, she notices things, she's more perceptive about things. She said to me the other day, 'Granny, you really like people, don't you? You really mind about people?' She was quite thoughtful and then she gave a list of things that she knew I had done, little things to do with people in the village. 'You really like people, don't you? I wish I did.' So I said, 'I think if you could talk to them a little more, and try to understand them and ask about them so that they talk to you, and always ask about things you think they might be interested in, then you'll get to know people more, and it becomes more interesting and you can also love people.' She thought a lot about it, but she didn't make any comment. But I think she understood. You don't get a response to a conversation at once, we'll get a second instalment later. It's like that with every subject; you say something and there's complete silence and then suddenly three weeks later you may be doing something else and she'll say, 'You know what you said, Granny?' She's a thinker, but a reserved and withdrawn thinker.

I've had them one at a time since they were quite small. I much prefer them on their own, you can imagine. That's not just practical, although I do get hammered to death when

I have the four of them, but they're different characters by themselves and that is when you really make your relationship. When you get them all together they're a little tribe, and like all tribes they are each of them trying to come up tops, and sometimes my courage fails and that's when, if I'm not terribly careful, I snap. And it's really because I can't cope with all four personalities together.

They've been taught from a very early age that they all have books at the end of their beds, and that when they wake up they can put on their dressing gowns and go downstairs to the loo, and then they go back to bed till I call and say it's time to get up. It means that the parents can sleep in at the weekends and it's no hardship. The three-year-old always has crayons and colouring books, and from a very early age they all know they stay in bed in the morning till it's time to get up. I think that's a wonderful rule, a number one rule! I go and call at the bottom of the stairs, 'You can get up!'

They like to choose their own clothes at a very early age. There's no point in putting them out overnight; they seem to know, to an alarming extent, what they want to wear. In fact, I despair about them thinking so much about how they look at such an early age. I find it narcissistic and it worries me sometimes, although I must say they're rather good at it, they know what matches. Anyhow they love to do it, plus their little beads and whatnots that they put on. Then they come down and we have breakfast together, and we talk about what we're going to do that day and about what I have to do. We divide the day into doing things that I've got to do that they can help me with and certain things that they can't help me with. I can say to them, 'Look, loves, I've got to do this. It will probably take about quarter of an hour, so will you go and read your book or play your game.' Then I set them up with their book or their game and they're pretty good.

I think my approach is quite organised, perhaps too organised for this generation. I know grandmothers are meant to be treats, and in a way they're treaty people: they're the ones who disobey the parents' rules about having brownies for tea when they don't have sweet things at home, but I don't think grannies should be just treat people. The children should realise you've got your own interests and there are times when it's wonderful to have them, but you've got to get on with your life, and they understand that. With four of them, it's helpful to the parents to have some rules, because I think the real function of grandparents is to support the parents – above all.

I've just had them for ten days so that David and Helen, in spite of the baby only being six months, can have ten days up in Scotland on their own. I think it's terribly hard to have a marital life with four children: I mean time to talk over the major problems and time to love each other without some interruption from somebody. I am the only surviving granny, so I try to have them twice a year for ten days. I have some help, I couldn't do it without help. Unfortunately my children married quite late. I should be doing all this at fifty, but I'm nearer seventy and that's the trouble! That's one drawback for women who go to university and have a career. They all get themselves into careers that they are fascinated by, so they don't marry till later. My sister-in-law is seventy-three and coping with her first grandchild, and she has all the same emotional feelings about it and desperately wants to do everything, but it's quite tough for her. She, like me goes to bed when the children go to bed. At half past seven you'll find me taking up my cup of tea and going to bed. [Lots of laughter] It's the only way I can survive when I have all of them.

I'm no good with my hands and I miss that. I've got a friend who is terribly good with her hands and she's always making things, and all her grandchildren from an early age made things. I never have been able to do it; I'm a fool about it, absolutely hopeless. I can't draw either and very soon the children learn how to draw much better than me. I find that a great lack. I share my love of the country and the seaside with them and we go to look for birds. They love the garden; they have their little packets of seeds and they put their seeds in and put the packet on a stick. They love washing up, which is hell! As they get down from the table they put their own things into the machine and everything that has to be washed by hand goes into a bowl.

They have a weekend cottage in the next village and I always do flowers, and we light the Aga for them and turn the heating on. I was very thrilled this weekend because Gemma, that's the three-year-old, loves to watch me do the flowers, and she suddenly turned to me and said, 'You haven't done the flowers this weekend, Granny.' This was the weekend I had the four of them, and I thought, 'Oh Lord!' and she said, 'I'll do them.' Well, she went into the garden and picked a few ghastly heads, the ones that were left, and stuffed them into a vase and put them on the kitchen table, and I thought, 'That's good, I've got that one across!'

I read to them a tremendous amount. Helen's marvellous at that. Whatever she's doing, and she's a jolly busy person, it's absolutely sacrosanct that she read for at least quarter of an hour a day to each child. It's such a pleasure.

Bath-time is the worst moment because I am tired by then. Perhaps if it were four lumps of soap and four flannels it would be easier, because they all bath together quite early at about 6.30, and then the older children stay up in their dressing gowns, Vera till half past eight and Magdalen till half past seven. But bath-time is a bad time for me, because they're tired and I'm tired and the toys all go into the bath. I don't really enjoy bath-time!

I made up a little song that I used to sing to all my children, a sort of goodnight lullaby. I was thrilled because Helen carried it on; she sings this mundane little dirge to all her children and they love it just like mine did, although it couldn't be more ordinary, so I have to sing that to them before they will go to sleep. And they've always had what we call 'lily-banks': when they put their heads down on the pillows, I push them round the backs of their heads, so they have a sense of security around their heads. So that has to be done.

I don't smack because Helen doesn't believe in it. *I* believe in it. [Lots of laughter] I do get cross and they know when I'm cross. It's difficult because one mustn't nag, and of course that's one of the big differences between our upbringing and theirs. In our family what grown-ups said went. If you were told to do something you did it. I don't want to sound smug about it, but you actually did it. There was no alternative, but now that doesn't happen. 'Go and wash your hands,' and absolutely nothing happens, and you feel rather helpless at that stage. Helen says, because mothers now are so close to the children and have them all around, you can't go on nagging, so if it doesn't happen you don't follow it up. Well, I'm not sure if she's right there, because there has to be quite a lot of bribery which sticks in my throat. So its 'If you do this, we'll go to the beach, and if you don't, we won't.' But then you're faced with the situation where one child didn't obey and you've got two children who did obey who are dying to go to the beach, and you were fool enough to make a condition which you've obviously got to break, because otherwise what are you going to do with the other two?

I always say, 'I have never had the breast of chicken.' The reason is that my parents always had the breast and we children were given the brown meat. Then my children were always given the breast and once more we had the brown meat. Now it's the grandchildren's turn for the breast. It's true: they do get the very best. I don't know if that's right.

You don't know what's going to happen to them in this life. They may not always be able to have the breast of chicken.

I think one's got to show them other sides of life. I did that too early with my own children and one must be careful about it. I was a governor of a mental hospital in those days, and I used to take my children with me on visiting days and I think it had a profound effect on them. I think I did it too early; they remember it with horror. I thought it was good for them to understand that not everybody was complete and perfect, but perhaps it was wrong, perhaps it was too soon. Looking back on it, I think they should know their own environment well before you introduce them to problems, otherwise you are going to shake them to the foundations. I think one of the most important things is confidence. I don't mean the over-confident because they're not the nicest people, but if you know who you are and what you feel, it's a good thing.

Basically Granny has one or two of her own rules and she has other little ways that are her ways, for instance one might say Grace. These can be accepted as Granny's ways, but I think in the major things you must follow exactly the line taken by the parents though you may not agree with it all. The main area you may not agree about is discipline. That's the hardest thing for the previous generation to grasp. I believe that if you don't have the discipline it's so hard to get things done, you waste so much time, but that may be survival, it may be my age group. I find children understand discipline and they don't resent it if it's done in a certain way. Manners is a difficult area. Children are often so spontaneous in their reactions. They come to see us, and, they rush past us to say 'Hello' to the dogs and they forget to say 'Hello' to us. I think as grandparents one has got to support parents; they have a difficult time with discipline when it's a very lively family with lots of interests.

I find this generation are marvellous to their friends, and

their friends are awfully important to them. They are much closer to their friends than we ever were because they are so much more honest, they tell each other what is happening and you can therefore support each other. I've said to Helen, who does have weekly help, 'I'll always cope with a crisis, and I'll always try somehow to do the ten days twice a year so you always get two really good breaks in the year.' But otherwise I think it's their life and I don't offer to help when one of them gets measles because I think that's part of family life; if you've got four children then you've got to cope with it. I don't offer to baby-sit, but I am there in crisis times – and they seem to crop up quite frequently.

When they come down for the weekends, I meet Helen and the younger children on Fridays and the older ones come down later with their father. We have tea together and talk over all the girlie things, that's marvellous! Then for the rest of the weekend we might not see them at all, or I might take two of them down to the beach, or we might have Sunday lunch, but I don't expect, just because they're close by, to see them every weekend, and I don't feel remotely hurt or uppity if the weekend goes by without seeing them again. I think it's important to leave them their privacy and not to interfere, because there is every opportunity to do so. You can always do with another pair of hands if you've got four children, but, as a grandmother, you mustn't overdo it if you want to do other things with your life. You forget the amount of energy you have now compared with what you did have. Luckily I can talk to Helen without any problem. I don't know if I shall be able to talk in the same way to my daughter-in-law, who has only just arrived on the scene and hasn't yet got any children.

I have constantly to reassess myself as a grandmother: why I do things, and why I keep on these little shibboleths and rituals and whether they're really right. But everyone has their 'ways', and I think it's good for the children to understand that and that they may have to fit in with someone else sometimes.

I think it's difficult how you give presents. It shouldn't really depend on what they've got, because it's lovely to have impulse things given to you – a little treat, but I try to think about it realistically. The little girls haven't got a Noah's Ark, so we're going to give them one for Christmas, a hand-made one. Instead of giving them each a present, they are going to have to understand this year that they will have one between them. It's the only way we can afford to get them a Noah's Ark, but I'm not looking forward to Christmas day. Sharing isn't easy to explain to children!

I love to look through my old books and decide which Vera is ready for and lend it to her. I keep a little note in my desk which we write together: 'Granny has loaned me *Doctor Dolittle* and it must come back again.' It goes in a little drawer until she returns the book, and then we tear it up and start again. It's partly organisation and partly to safeguard those books for the next grandchild. It's very easy with the first one to overdo it completely because you're so thrilled, and you've got so many ideas about what you might give them, and I think it's important not to get carried away. Books and possessions should be valued and shared; there are going to be others who want to use them. You don't want to be popular all the time, you just want to be ordinary, otherwise they only like you for what you give them, but perhaps I overdo it the other way.

I've got a secondhand cot and a high chair which belonged to my children, but I've hung on to them because it's so much easier to have your own equipment. I'm surprised you've got a playpen, Nell, because the thinking of this generation seems to be that playpens are awful and nobody must have one, children must be allowed freedom of movement. I say that if you put all their toys in a playpen so that they can get at what they want, then they're perfectly happy to spend an hour in the mornings safely, while you do other things. Otherwise you're on tenterhooks all the time watching that child. But they're very unpopular with this generation of mothers and, unless his mother does it too, when you come to put your grandson in the playpen you're going to have hell! [Lots of laughter] I had to abandon the playpen; it's a real tragedy.

I have much closer relationships with my grandchildren than my grandmother had with me, much more demonstrative. We share their lives, and when we have them on their own it is totally absorbing and we are wholly responsible, whereas my grandmother never looked after our physical needs. I felt closer to my grandmother between the ages of about nine and twelve before I went to boarding school than I ever did to my mother. My grandmother set aside time for us, whereas my mother never did anything specifically with us. She was very artistic, but she was trapped by my father's illness. He was badly wounded in the First World War and never fully recovered. Even in those days when people didn't show their feelings and certainly didn't talk about them, I was aware of my mother's frustration. It did affect us.

Now, at Christmas, my sister and I still say the same poems and sing the songs we learnt from my grandmother, and the children beg us to do it. We pop up from behind the sofa and they scream with laughter. It was the only time as children we could really let ourselves go. I still have my grandmother's musical box and when my grandchildren come to stay, we dance to the tunes. It's full of waltzes. [At this point Ursula gets up to illustrate and does some very graceful pirouettes.] We do low vees, [she puts her feet in fifth position and joins her hands in a garland] and high vees [she reverses her feet and lifts her hands over her head]. Sometimes we put on a record of *Swan Lake* and dance to that, and they all love doing that. If you could see me, this galloping, galumphing elephant! Mercifully they're not critical. Robert is the one who is knowledgeable about music, and he plays things like *Peter and the Wolf*, and then he talks to the children about the instruments and the theory of music, and he plays the piano and sings with them. When we had Dorothy's christening in a little church on the cliffs, Vera decided she wanted to sing a hymn. We were amazed because she is so shy, but she and Magdalen sang absolutely in tune, so perhaps there is a musical strain that goes through.

Cato is naughty and we go out to tea

CATO HAS CAUGHT on to being naughty. The first time I had to tell him off for taking unlit coal out of the fire. I put it back, saying 'No,' and carried him to the other side of the room and gave him a toy to distract him. Directly I was looking away, back he crawled to the fire and took out the coal. I did the same thing again, but this time I watched him and, when he got to the fire and stretched out his hand, I said, 'No,' quite firmly. His hand stopped in mid-air and his back went quite stiff. After a moment his hand went out again rather tentatively towards the coal. 'No!' I said, more strongly this time. His hand dropped and he began to howl, the loudest howl you ever heard. I picked him up and hugged him.

Later we were in the kitchen; I was making lunch and he was playing with the pots and pans. He navigated the two steps and crawled away towards the sitting room. A minute or two later I went to see what was going on and found he had filled the dogs' water jug with coal. 'Cato!' I yelled and he looked apprehensive, so I showed him how to put the damp coals back, scooped him up and took him into the kitchen for lunch. I plonked him on his chair on top of three telephone books. He pulls the tablecloth towards him, nearly upsetting my plate, and when I tell him not to do it he does it again, looking me challengingly in the eye the while. I have a moment of panic. How do I deal with this? I say, 'No,' as firmly as I can. He looks at me, his mouth full of boil-in-the-bag chicken and rice, and spits the mouthful on to the floor. 'That's very naughty,' I say, and pick it up and put it back in his bowl before May and Ivy eat it. I look at him and he stares back at me as if to say 'Well?' I feel his will crunch up against mine. I get a banana and slice it for him, avoiding his eyes. He has defied me, not once but three times, and I am rattled, but I think about May and Ivy, and how sometimes Ivy, the 'good' one, loves to be naughty, to break out of her goodness. When I call May out of the wood, Ivy will dash back past May and incite her to run away just to cause a disruption and leave me cross and shouting. Perhaps Cato is like Ivy, good at heart but needing a rumpus now and then to add a bit of spice to life. Later I tell my friend Rebecca, and she laughs and says, 'James does the same and it shows he has spirit.' I relax in her optimism.

In the afternoon, we go with Joy to visit Sharon and Wayne. Wayne is a firecracker and, although he is three months younger than Cato, he has been walking since he was nine months old, and now he can run and dance and jump. Cato is astonished and very impressed. I loved us being together on an adventure in a strange house, him and me out together in the big wide world. He sits on my knee wide-eyed and, when I lift Wayne on to my other knee, he leans towards him and kisses him to show his respect. Soon they are playing together with a telephone on the kitchen floor. Sharon, handing over to Joy her new fifteen-day-old baby, Carmel, puts on the kettle.

Cissy, Joy's mother, arrives and Wayne runs to greet her at the door. She picks him up, but he wriggles to get down and goes immediately to her handbag to get her lipstick. Cissy dances the cha-cha-cha to get his attention so Joy can rescue her handbag. She swings her hips and moves her feet, her thin legs stiff like stalks on a frosty morning emerging from the flowery shrub of her cotton dress. Soon all three babies are being jiggled on different knees, tea is being drunk, cake eaten, gossip exchanged, and Cato and I are happy.

He falls asleep on the way back to my house and when he wakes up he doesn't want his high tea of baked beans on toast. I take him home to his mother. He is tired and cries in her arms. I am worried, but she says reassuringly, 'Don't worry, it's the grannies; he always has too exciting a time when he goes out with the grannies and comes back exhausted.' She takes off his socks and seeing his dirty little feet she says, 'Cato, where did you get such dirty feet?' I slip quickly out of the door.

CHAPTER 8

Chrissie

CHRISSIE IS MARRIED to Ron. *They have a daughter called Debbie, who is married to Terry, and they have two small children called Hayley and Little Terry. Chrissie has auburn hair. She is slender and pretty, and wears high heeled shoes and is a snappy dresser. She will be forty-seven years old this birthday. She lives near the gates of Richmond Park on a Sixties' prize-winning council estate. I met Chrissie with Joy; they grew up in the same street and have been best friends since they were six. Now we sit in Joy's flat, we three women and Hayley who's come with her nan.*

Throughout the conversation, Hayley, who has long curly hair, long curly eyelashes, big brown eyes and the plumpest legs you ever set eyes on, is caressed, her toes nibbled, her curls arranged and rearranged, told to 'pipe down' or 'shut up', to 'be a good girl for her nan, or Nanny won't buy her any sweeties on the way home,' but Hayley continues to put her plump little hand across Chrissie's mouth, crawl up Chrissie's back using her hair as a climbing rope, whisper in her ear and generally make her presence felt. All this is water off a duck's back to Chrissie who goes on telling her story.

I never knew my mother's mother. She lived and died in Ireland, and we never had the money to go. I'll tell you what, though, I would love to have gone over and met her.

My father's mother was called Susan and we lived with her in Fulham. She lived on the ground floor. She had the front room with the green settee and the piano, and you went down a step into the kitchen, and beyond that was the scullery, and the toilet was in the back garden. Then up two flights of stairs, Uncle Ernie slept in the back room and Nanny Susan had the front room. Then there were two little rooms on the top floor; my mum and my dad slept in one room and we three girls in the other. I was one end of the bed, Maureen was the other end and Gladys on a mattress over there. Don't forget there was no electricity, none at all. We had the old-fashioned gas mantles that you had to light with a match.

The cooker was on the landing and it was freezing cold. If you wanted to fill the kettle, you had to go downstairs to the landing below where there was an old butler sink and a cold tap. We had to go out to the garden to use the toilet, but you couldn't do that of a night-time, you had to use the bucket.

My Dad died when I was nine. He used to work over at Chelsea football ground. I can remember him as if it was yesterday, lying on the settee with the death rattle going in this throat and my mother trying to give him a cup of tea, but his hands were that swollen he couldn't get his finger through the handle. My mum was crying and Maureen, she was fourteen, was crying and my Gladys was crying. He died at half past six in the morning and Maureen couldn't go to work that day.

My grandmother had no time for my mum. My mum worked down the school scrubbing floors and they come up white as your tablecloth. We never had lino or carpet down our stairs, but my mum used to scrub them and she had the whitest front step in the street. My nan never helped her, she was very hard. When we came home from school and my mum was out at work, we'd never know if there was going to be even a piece of bread and marge to eat. My nan had a great big old-fashioned radio, but she didn't ever say, 'Come in, loves, I'll make you a cup of tea, and you can listen to the radio till you mum comes in and have a bit of bread and butter.' No, we had to go upstairs and there would be the table with the newspaper on it and the bread and the marge, the jam, the milk and the sugar; there was no cup-board for anything to go in. What food there was was put on that table and that was it. The only time she made a fuss of me was when I made my Holy Communion and that was because she could show people my photo. I had long curly auburn hair right down my back and I held a prayer book and a white rosary. She died a few years later, but I never really missed her.

When I was nineteen and I got pregnant, my auntie said to me, 'Are you going to get married?' 'No, I'm not,' I said. 'Your grandmother would turn in her grave,' she said. 'Well,' I says, 'let her turn!' She never done nothing for my mum – she was an old cow. I can see her standing there, tall, like a sergeant major; she'd frighten the life out of you as soon as look at you.

MY GRANDCHILDREN

I see them every single day; every single day Debbie comes over with the two of them. They only live five minutes away and they always have their dinner over my house. I cook the dinner and them three sit down, and I'm running round doing my greens and potatoes ready for the night-time before I go back and clean the school, and then I come home and have my dinner with Ron of a night-time. When they're this age your time is literally taken up with them all the time. When she comes over, I says, 'Have they had their lunch?' and she says 'No,' so I find something in the fridge, and I cut the potatoes up ever so small and a bit of cabbage ever so small. Hayley is nineteen months old, so she feeds herself and she's no trouble, but Little Terry is only ten months and he is inclined to cry while we're having our lunch. I make do with a bit of potato in the bread while they're being fed, and I'm clearing up at the same time. I like to get them two fed and then Debbie to sit down and have her bit of lunch, and then I know she's had something to eat.

Really and truly Debbie went in at the deep end. She'd no sooner had Hayley than she fell for Little Terry. He was early so there's only nine months between them. Go back three years and Debbie was at home, and she never knew what it was to lift a cup from the table to the side. Everything was done for her – washing, ironing – but she used to do her bedroom on a Saturday, that was the only thing she'd do. She'd come home from work and her dinner was ready, and then she'd go up and have her bath. So in the space of three years everything has been turned upside down for her and that's the reason I have her over every day to give her that bit of a break. It's not much of a break, but she can sit and have a sandwich and a cup of tea, and I take charge of the kids for her.

When Debbie was carrying Hayley, those nine months seemed like nine years, but with the second one the time zoomed by. Hayley was born on 17 April at seventeen minutes past one, and by the time I got up there all Terry's family was there. When I think back, I was a bit awful – my sister-in-law wanted to pick her up and Debbie said, 'No, no one is picking her up!' I said 'Don't be so horrible. If people want to pick her up, they can pick her up.' And of course I'm talking about an hour after the baby was born and you are a bit watery-eyed and that, and then I felt sorry for her.

When she had Terry nine months later, she said, 'I don't want no visitors till the next day.' Her water broke the week before and it was only Joy who made her go to the doctor's. She don't always listen to me. I could say to her, supposing the baby had a sore bum for instance, 'Now don't always use that zinc and caster – use Vaseline,' and she'd say, 'No, she's having zinc and caster.' Then Joy would come along with a big jar of Vaseline and say, 'Put this on her,' and she'd do it straightaway.

When I first saw Hayley, I was so pleased, I really was, not because she's mine but she was beautiful born. She was eight pounds, and she had a load of black hair and pinky cheeks, and she was really, really lovely. I couldn't wait for her to come home. When she come home, I couldn't wait for her to wake up. I'd sit and watch her in the pram, and I'd say, 'She's awake!' I couldn't wait to get hold of her. I wanted her as *my* baby, so to speak.

When she came to me and once she was over the four weeks mark, I started her off on her rusks. When she got to four months, I gave her a bit of mashed potato and gravy. When your baby comes to you, take him off his mum, let his mum have five minutes in the chair, and you feed him, you do his bum. If he's got a sore bum, wipe it with a drop of water, and then leave him with no nappy on and let him kick, but if he gets the colic watch him. If he gets the colic, his toilet will be really green and then all he wants is nothing but boiled water for twenty-four hours. Once he's over that and he's on the road to recovery, then all he wants is plenty of love and a lot of fuss made of him.

Debbie told me that Big Terry said to her one day, 'Your mum thinks it's her baby. She should realise it's our baby!' That was in the beginning when it was all new to us, but now Big Terry will phone me and say, 'Do you want a pest for the night?' Now he says, 'We're lucky with your mum round the corner,' because I have them over every day even on a Sunday.

I love having her on a Saturday night, don't get me wrong, but the only thing is she wakes me up early on a Sunday morning and that's the only day I get a lie-in, because all the other mornings I get up at five to go early-morning cleaning. On a normal Sunday I lay in till about half past eight or nine, and then I phone Debbie up and say, 'When she's had her nap, give me a ring and I'll come and pick her up.' She usually rings about half twelve, and I go and get her and I keep her till about eight o'clock; it all depends if she's getting too irritable. If she is, then I bring her back over, wash her face and her hands, do her bum and make sure she has a bit of tea, some bread and butter or whatever, and then I say, 'I'm going to go now,' and she starts crying, yeah, she cries after me when I go.

Next year Little Terry will be old enough to come over too and I'm looking out for a double pushchair. I don't want to buy a new one, so I'm looking out for a second-hand one. I want to give Debbie a break, and then give her a bit of liver and bacon, or fish fingers and chips, so she has a bit of a sit-down in the middle of the day. She's only in the one-bedroomed flat, don't forget.

When Debbie was born, I never had no patience with her at all. I never had two bob's worth of patience. I was terrible. I was so poor I had to borrow my mum's bar of soap to wash the nappies; I'd put them in the bucket and boil them up. My sink and cooker were out on the landing. We were living in one room and didn't have a kitchen or bathroom, or anything like that. As you opened the door you was in the room and that was it. When Debbie was five or six, she had long hair down her back. I was brushing it one morning, and she was crying and I was so wild, I got hold of the brush and I brushed her face like that and made all red marks.

I think myself I've got more time with these two because I didn't have a lot of time with Debbie. Ron was in the nick at the time and everything was on my shoulders. I was only nineteen and I had no money; I wasn't working, all I was getting was five pounds and sixpence off the Social and living in one room. I had no television, I was carrying the coal in big bags up ninety stairs. The only clothes I had was what I stood up in. Joy gave me the coat off her back, or I wouldn't have had a coat. Joy got all the good gear off the W V S.

You see all these films about how wonderful husbands are, and I expected that life and I didn't have it. Ron was a very selfish person. I remember once he won a hundred pounds: it was a lot of money in those days, and I wanted some brassieres and drawers and Debbie needed a coat and he give me ten pounds to buy the lot, and he went out and bought himself two new suits, a black pinstripe and a grey pinstripe, and when you see him out you'd say, 'Blimey, he's got a few bob!' Very smart, very, very smart. But he's only got what he stands up in now. I've got more than what he has, the boot's on the other foot now. He's got two pairs of grey trousers that he's had for I don't know how long and one blue jacket, and the jacket must be nine years old and the boots that are on his feet are what I bought him for six quid.

I was working in the school kitchen and I bought a stand-up old-fashioned boiler off of someone. It was electric, but you had to put the washing in the boiler, lift it from the boiler into the spinner, spin your hot water out, then put that hot water back in the boiler, then run a hose or keep putting bowls of water in your spin-dryer to rinse it. When I think back, the kids today wouldn't put up with what we put up with. If Debbie has an argument with Terry, she says, 'Well, I'm going back to my mum's!'

As much as I moan about the kids – and sometimes I do

because I get very tired because I'm up at quarter to six and out to clean the school, then I'm home and straighten up and make a bit of dinner, then I've got my solicitor two afternoons a week – I clean his place – well, by the time I've lifted the two kids up two flights of stairs and she carries the pushchair up, time you do a bit of lunch for them, then sometimes I won't have time to make myself a cup of tea till three o'clock in the afternoon, and sometimes she'll say to me, 'Oh, Mum, you do shout and bawl,' and I say, 'Debbie, you've got to realise . . .' – but then if I were ever to tell them not to come over, I'd feel awful, I'd start thinking, 'Have they had their lunch?' Debbie's a good little mum, she really is, I'm quite surprised at her really.

On Friday the girl on the landing come for a packet of sugar, so I give her the sugar, then I done fish fingers and chips and, instead of putting the grill pan back under where it should go, I left it on top for a minute because I was going to take the crumbs out. With Hayley being under my feet as I've gone by, I've knocked the handle and it's gone flying, spilling all the crumbs on the floor. It's frightened her, but in a temper I got hold of her and put her out in the passage, like that. 'Bleeding kids,' I said, 'over here every day, I don't want you over next week!' But as quick as I've said it, straightened up the crumbs and put the grill pan away, I picked her up and cuddled her. She was crying and she went to slap me: 'Nan, Nan, Nan!' I said to her, 'Nan's naughty, but Nan was so bleeding tired!' I really was tired. Sometimes I don't even get a chance to sit down from getting back from my morning job and starting out again in the afternoon. And by the time I get home in the evening I've got to do the dinner then. It is a long day. Sometimes I think to myself, 'I wish they weren't coming over,' but when you see them. She runs along the landing calling, 'Nan!' And she knows where her bowl is and she wants her spoon. And you forget you're tired.

My Debbie was always crying, she was a right miserable kid. When she was carrying, all I said was, 'Well, I hope this one isn't like you, or she'll go straight over that balcony!' As luck would have it she's got two good kids. When I think back Debbie was probably half-starved, because we didn't have the money to feed them. What money you got, you'd buy a bit of grub with, but I didn't know one thing from another. Maybe she was hungry. Then I had the time for her, but I didn't have the patience. Now I've got loads of patience with these two and if I had another cot I'd take the two of them on a Saturday night to give Debbie a little lie-in on a Sunday.

When you was young if you wasn't going out you thought you was missing something. It was boring being stuck with the kids when you was young. As I am now, I've got my own few bob coming in the door, I can go over and get those two kids when I want to. I can go out and spend my money or stay at home. I'd like a new three-piece suite and some other bits and pieces, but you can carry on and carry on wanting this and wanting that, but it's only now these kids are little that I'm going to have them round me and I'd rather spend my money on them. I've always made sure I've got a hundred pounds in the bank for emergencies. As for the rest of what I earn, I spend it.

They went down to their other grandmother's house last Sunday and it worries the life out of me because they've got two great big Alsatians down there. I said to Debbie, 'Now don't start going there every Sunday, or I'll tell you what'll happen, I'm going to be the granny that's given them every‑thing – I've put their home together, it's not the best home, but what's in it I've mainly put in it, and I've always got a bit of dinner for them – and they're not going to bother to come over no more.' 'Oh no,' says Debbie, 'that'll never happen.' But when Hayley phones me up on the Monday, it's 'Nanny got this, Nanny got that . . .' I *was* cross. I turned round and I said, 'Who's your best nanny then?' Because I sing to her and I dance for her, and if I'm doing the potatoes and she says, 'I help Nanny,' then I always give her a potato and a blunt knife.

Then I asked Debbie straight out: 'What did *she* give you for dinner then?' Well, Debbie says she gave them a proper dinner: two boiled potatoes, two roast, a spoonful of peas and a bit of meat and gravy. I said, 'Well, where's their Yorkshire? Where's their carrots?' And then it turned out she gave them nothing for their tea! Well, if they're coming over to me, they'll have a bit of corned beef and some oven chips for their tea or some sausages, and if I make a bit of stew tonight I'll put some by for those children tomorrow.

So I said to Debbie, 'I'm telling you now, they'll know me more than they will her,' because I've got two rooms upstairs, I've got a cot there for the baby and a Put-U-Up bed for Hayley. Their other nan is what I call a 'Sunday nanny.' She'll have them down once every six or seven weeks – that's a Sunday nan. They've moved down to Ewell and bought their own house, and they pulled all the cork tiles off the bedroom walls in their council flat and took them with them, they even took the sink unit. That's the type of people they are.

I don't think I'd run off with a rich man now, because if I went on his yacht for six months the kids might not know me. No, I think I'll stay as I am in that respect. It would probably be lovely the first couple of months, but then you'd say, 'I don't know, this is a bit boring.'

CHAPTER 9

Jackie

JACKIE LIVES WITH her husband, Frank, a writer who has Parkinson's disease. They have three children: Paul, married to Viviana; Joanna, married to Ian; and Julia, their youngest daughter, or as Jackie says, 'Last but certainly not least!' Joanna and Ian have a son, Stefan Thomas, Jackie's first grandchild. Paul and Viviana have a daughter, Rafaella Sybil Maddalena, born this summer.

Jackie works for the Glastonbury Tourist Information Centre one day a week. She did English Literature 'A' level at evening classes this year. 'When I saw the list, I couldn't resist. It was Hamlet *and* Richard II, *two of my favourite Shakespeare plays,* Persuasion *and* Wuthering Heights, *two of my favourite novels, and Wilfred Owen, one of my favourite poets, and Chaucer who I'd never read before.' [She passed grade C.]*

I hadn't met Jackie before we got together to talk about grandmothers, but I'd known her brother for a long time.

MY MATERNAL GRANDMOTHER

My mother's mother was more important to me because she lived with us. She was born in Danzig and came to London in the 1880s because the Jews were being persecuted in Poland. There was an enormous emigration; everybody wanted to go to the United States and a lot of people who

[113]

thought they were going there ended up elsewhere. Polish would have been her language, but all the Jews spoke Yiddish to each other then. Yiddish went right across the world; it's the language that all Jews of that generation could understand each other in. By the time it got to my generation it had gone.

My mother was devoted to her parents. She got engaged at eighteen and married at twenty and it never occurred to her to leave them. They set up house together in King Edward Road in Hackney where my brother and I were born and later they moved west. I used to call Golders Green the furthest outpost of the Jewish Empire. We moved to a beautiful house in Cricklewood, which I loved.

My grandfather was an absolute devil with women. He had enormous charm and was wonderful with children. He died when I was four and nobody told me and I thought he had deserted me. I used to say, 'Where is Grandpa?' and they would say, 'He's gone to Poland to see his relations.' And I thought, 'How could he do that and not write to me?' I found out he was dead because when I was seven, I found a photograph of his grave with a stone edifice of an engraved book with my name on it. I was supposed to have dedicated this memorial to a grandfather I didn't even know was dead. That was one of my abiding childhood memories.

My mother always worked. They were fishmongers, and my mother was at the cash desk and my grandfather and father went to Billingsgate at five every morning. I remember my grandfather sitting in a chair once and saying, 'I'm so tired. Will someone cut off my hands and take them and wash them for me.'

We had a nanny, so we had this extraordinary English middle-class upbringing in a nice house with a nice garden, and our parents and grandparents were Jewish fishmongers – immigrant Jewish fishmongers – and we were always short of money. There was a constant worry about money.

My grandmother was a reserved woman. She had great dignity and was very strong. She didn't have a great deal to say to me because her English was imperfect so we didn't talk much. She kept a totally strict kosher household where we had two kitchens, two lots of cutlery and two lots of plates, and anything that touched meat never touched milk. I remember knives sticking out of the earth in a flowerbed and saying to my grandmother, 'What's that?' A milk knife had been put in the meat drawer by mistake and it had to be put in the earth for a month to cleanse it. She wore long dresses and had *pince-nez* and a bun, and she spoke very quietly, but she presided over everything. She did the cooking and we had all these Jewish rituals. She had a pair of doves and a dovecote and when they mated she named their offspring after members of the royal family, so the first pair were George and Mary. She had an enormous sense of repose. My mother often said to me, 'I don't know, Jac, but you're not a bit like me. You're far more like my mother!' She didn't get into a flap or get over-excited, and she didn't show what she felt about things very much and I'm the same. There was a strong allegiance between the females in the house and we ganged up on the men.

One of my most vivid memories was being alone one afternoon with my grandmother in the drawing room. The blinds were pulled down because she had a headache. She had put slices of lemon on her forehead and when she felt better she propped herself up and read a Yiddish newspaper. Suddenly she took a hairpin from her bun and started very deliberately poking it through the paper. I went over to see what she was doing, and there was a picture of a man and she was putting her hairpin through his eyes, puncturing them, I said, 'What are you doing?' She said, 'This is Hitler and he is very bad.' She was such a gentle and quiet person and I saw her rage.

The funny thing was that, because I had been brought up

in this very Jewish atmosphere, I terribly envied the girls in the school stories I read, *Dimsey at St Bride's* or whatever it is, and I thought their lives must be tremendously uncomplicated not being Jewish. I did so envy people who weren't Jewish, because I thought they had such an easy time of it. I wanted to be the same as everyone else.

I can remember my grandmother's death very clearly. She had a big bow-fronted bedroom in the front of the house and she was confined to bed. It was my eighth birthday and more than anything else I wanted a Shirley Temple doll and I got her from my grandmother. I went in to see her, and she was lying in bed and she didn't look any different. I went in holding my doll to say 'Thank you.' She looked very pleased. Two days later I was in the garden and I heard my mother crying. I knew what it meant and I thought, 'Grandma has died and they won't tell me unless I make them. And I'm going to make them tell me.' I was very anxious that people should be honest with me for once. Nanny came out into the garden with tears in her eyes and I could hear my mother sobbing. I looked at Nanny very hard and I said, 'How's Grandma?' and she said, 'She's dead.' And I thought, 'Thank goodness she's told me.'

I wasn't allowed to go to the funeral. I was sent for the day to my aunt's house and I came home when it was all over. I remember sitting in the dining room. There was a big plane tree outside the window and I had this feeling about what happened when you went to heaven. I sat every day in this chair and looked out of the window at the plane tree and tried to imagine how far she'd got. Had she got to the top of the branches yet or was she still hovering in the foliage? And every day I got her a little further in her ascent into heaven, until I thought she'd finally reached it.

The atmosphere in the house changed enormously. She was a matriarch and when she was gone who was to take her place? She was a woman of the household and she was the head of that household, and she held things together for all of us. After she died things disintegrated.

MY PATERNAL GRANDMOTHER

My paternal grandmother was a different kettle of fish. Those grandparents lived about a mile away and every Sunday we would set out on the walk with my heart getting deeper and deeper into my boots. It was a small house near Child's Hill. We'd go in and there would be a room full of identical men smiling at us, because my father had six brothers who all looked alike. Instead of saying, 'Hello, I'm Uncle Harry,' they'd say, 'Do you know who I am?' I'd be panic-stricken in case I said the wrong one. My grandfather was very religious: they went to the synagogue wearing top hats, and he was very stern and totally unloving. The moment I arrived he would take down a Hebrew book and say, 'Read to me.' I understand from my mother that my grandmother loathed him. He gave her a child every two years. She had one daughter, poor woman, and seven sons. He was a tailor and they were as poor as church mice.

My grandmother gathered her sons about her on Sunday afternoons and spilled venom at them for two hours, my mother always said. They went on their own and she would, one by one, subtly point out the shortcomings of their wives, get them all in a turmoil and then they would go home and be beastly to their wives.

My grandfather committed suicide in 1939 – I believe he hanged himself. I remember a telephone call and my father rushing out. I adored playing the piano; we were taking in German refugees as paying guests and the one we had at the time was a young pianist, who was teaching me. Later my father came into the drawing room where I was happily practising, and banged the lid down and said, 'You won't be playing that for a year.' Very strict mourning was adhered to, where you had no music and no entertainment, and my parents wore black for the first six months and grey for the next six months. So there went the piano, and I resented my grandfather for dying and stopping me playing.

My grandmother went on as before. She never made a fuss of me. She dispensed tea, that's about all I can remember her doing. If she visited us in our house, she always gave me half a crown, which was a lot in those days. The only thing I remember her saying was when my mother offered her tea, she'd say, 'Don't vorry abaht me.' Her English wasn't good; she always spoke Yiddish to her own family. When she came to see us, she behaved like the visiting queen, she was very regal and wore a lot of satin and carried a fan. She wasn't a nice woman, but I don't think it was her fault. She'd married a man who was a religious maniac and quite brutal, not in a physical but in a mental sense. She lived in abject poverty when she was young because of all these children that she didn't want, and there wasn't a lot of love in that household.

When I was getting married, I was summoned to her and she said, 'I'd like to give you a present.' She offered me a choice between a rather dreadful 1930s cut-glass dressing-table set and a silver-plate tea service where the water jug and the tea pot didn't quite match. I thought at least I could make tea in the tea pot. She died when she was well into her eighties, but it is sad in a way that there was so very little relationship between us.

✗

THE BIRTH OF MY GRANDCHILD

I was certain that Joanna would never have a child. She loathed babies – she poked them and called them 'it'. I said to her when she got married, 'If you don't have babies, don't think you're going to get any nagging from me, because I don't think it's your bag at all.' It only shows how wrong you can be, because she's a wonderful mother and incredibly patient.

Stefan's birth was almost as dramatic as Paul's. Paul's was a last-minute Caesarian when I was warned that he might not survive. Stefan's was not as bad as that, but Joanna is very tiny – she's even shorter than I am – the baby was in a breech position, it was the end of September and the baby was due in November. She was still working and they hadn't been in their flat very long so she was still buying things for it. She went into a shop in Covent Garden to get some artificial fruit and felt her waters go. She said to the girl, 'Excuse me, but do you mind if I ring my husband, because I think I'm about to have a baby.' The girl was shocked because Joanna didn't look pregnant. Joanna rang Ian, who couldn't get a taxi, so he ran all the way from the office in D'Arblay Street and met Joanna, and they got in a taxi to St Mary's (where all my children were born, so it was a lovely continuation). The people at the hospital said 'It's all right, it's only the front waters that have gone' – (I didn't know there was any difference) – 'and it's just a leak and will seal itself up,' because she was six weeks early. However, they suggested she stay in overnight. She went home to get some things, and rang me and told me what was happening and said, 'I'll give you a ring in the morning when I come out.'

For some reason it didn't occur to me she was going to have the baby. It was six weeks early and she was bound to be late, and I'd already booked Frank for his yearly check-up with his neurologist for November 9, because by then the baby would be here and we could kill two birds with one stone, so there was no way she was going to have that baby at the end of September as far as I was concerned. When we went to bed, Frank suggested we take the mobile phone into the bedroom with us, but I said, 'No, whatever for?' He said, 'Supposing Ian rings in the night and we don't hear it?' And I said, 'Why should Ian ring? She'll be out tomorrow.' That was it as far as I was concerned and we went to bed.

In the middle of the night Frank said, 'Jackie?' He never calls me, he just speaks in his normal voice as if it wasn't four o'clock in the morning, and I hear him say, 'Jackie, I think I heard the phone ring.' I said, 'What? I didn't hear it.' And he said, 'Well, I did, and it's stopped now.' I said, 'Oh my God, do you think it was Ian?' He said, 'Well, I think perhaps you should find out.' And I said, 'Well, I can't ring somebody at four o'clock in the morning. Supposing it wasn't him?' And Frank said, 'Who else is it likely to have been!' So I got up and rang, and Ian answered and I said, 'Ian, did you ring?' Ian said. 'Yes, I'm just on my way to the hospital: Joanna's in labour.'

Well, we didn't go back to sleep. I had no idea it was going to hit me like that. Apart from everything else, Joanna had never been as close to me as Paul and particularly Julia. She's always been Frank's daughter in her personality and her looks and in every way she was Frank's adored baby right from the word go. They adored each other when she was a little girl and they still do. So I didn't really think it was going to hit me like this. (Incidentally Joanna and I are now closer than we've ever been.) I didn't sleep another wink, and at seven o'clock Ian rang and said all was still in progress and he'd ring again when there was any news. Frank and I just sat and looked at each other. I couldn't do a thing. I don't think we ate anything, we just sat. At about eleven o'clock he rang again and said it was a bit hairy because the baby was breech, but that she was doing okay and that she'd had an epidural. I asked, 'Are they going to do a Caesar?' And he said, 'They're making up their minds if they need to do one or not.'

I assumed they'd do a Caesar – after all, I'd had one and she was even smaller than I was – so I spent the next two hours trying to imagine what was happening to her from the way it had happened to me: the operating theatre and the prick in the arm, except when Paul was born it was the mask straight over the face because they were all in such a hurry, and wondering if they could do the Caesar with an epidural or whether she'd have to have a general anaesthetic. We still didn't eat, we didn't speak to each other at all. We were both completely locked in our separate worlds and concentrating on Joanna and this baby. We had decided that as soon as we knew anything definite we would leave for London, so the only thing I did do was ring a friend and say, 'For God's sake, get down here and look after the cats.' I won't leave my cats alone. At about one o'clock Ian rang with his voice bubbling and bursting and said, 'Everything's all right and it's a boy and we're calling him Stefan Thomas!' I said, 'How much does he weigh?' expecting him to say six or seven pounds, and he said, 'Four pounds.' It was stupid really, I knew he was six weeks premature, but I didn't expect him to weigh four pounds. They eased him out: she didn't need a Caesarian after all. He was born bottom first with his legs wrapped round his head, but they didn't need forceps, they did a beautiful job. He was in such good shape he didn't even need an incubator.

I called my next-door neighbour, and Frank and I burst into tears and hugged each other, and then we set off for London. I remember I played a tape of the Vivaldi 'Gloria' in the car over and over again. I drove to London, tears streaming down my face: grandparents suddenly, a grand-mother. We arrived on the dot of six o'clock outside St Mary's. God was with us, because someone drew away from a meter just as we drew up. We dashed up to the maternity unit. Joanna was lying in bed with this tiny creature cupped in her arms. There she was with this little tiny thing with a little hat on his head – it was a bit of bandage pulled over his head with a little point on it like a pixie. And he lay there and I fell in love. I just looked at him and I fell in love. He seemed to me the most perfect creature. I couldn't believe it.

I've always been a great admirer of A. S. Neill, partly because I had been brought up in such a religious and guilt-ridden household. I think I spent my entire childhood feeling guilty about something, so my own children weren't going to have any of that. I wanted freedom but not licence for them. I hate children who are arrogant, but on the other hand I do like children who are open and easy, so Neill suited me well and I used to go down to Summerhill to see what was going on. My mother used to say, 'If you don't believe in smacking him, you're making a rod for your own back.' And I would say, 'No, I'm going to do it my way.' Now with my grandson, I don't want to be an indulgent granny. I don't want him to look at me and see a bag of sweets. So I'm a book granny, every time I see him I bring him a book.

When they come down to stay, I'm shattered. This child is not a walking disaster area, but just a volcano which erupts in the house. We're having a week's holiday with them in Suffolk later this summer. Joanna said, 'I had such happy holidays in Suffolk. Stefan's got to have happy holidays in Suffolk. Let's all go there.' So we've taken a cottage.

Stefan likes me very much. He always has. When they came down the first Christmas, he was three months old and when we met them at the station he beamed. Of course, he only sees me once a month and he also has to cope with three people in his life, because Joanna is back at work and Fay looks after him in the day-time. He knows his aunts and uncle, and when Joanna showed him my photograph the other day she said, 'Jac,' and he said, 'Jac!' so I have a feeling I'm going to be 'Jac'. But he's not ready yet to be left on his own with me. He copes very well with everything, but he's not ready to take anyone else on board. We have baby-sitted him when he was younger, but now he's going through a stage of wanting to be with Joanna or Ian or Fay, his nanny, and I understand that very well.

X

AFTER THE HOLIDAY

The week in Suffolk with Stefan was a huge success. Paul and Vivi, who was eight months pregnant, were there too. I talked to Stefan a lot and he looked at me and listened, and I used quite grown-up words, and I heard Paul say to Vivi, 'Mum really talks to Stefan; there's none of this baby language or talking down, that's the way to do it,' and I thought, 'Hurray, he approves of something I'm doing.'

I gave Stefan his breakfast every morning. He has the most gargantuan appetite and having had his own breakfast, he would then share mine; I lost half a stone in a week. We put telephone books on the chair and he sat next to me. The moment we got there (I don't know where I got this idea that he wouldn't want to go anywhere alone with me), a hand was slipped into mine and I was pulled down to what he called the seashore. He loved going to feed the ducks on the mere and, as he lives in a flat, he loved being out of doors. He was usually in bed by about 9.30 and then the grown-ups could talk, or watch telly or whatever. So we had lovely out-of-door days; he's a very adaptable child. He's not at all like his uncle Paul; he's a practical little boy, very different from Paul whose babyhood I remember very well as he was my first child.

By the end of the week together our relationship was totally established, we were really close. When we got home and telephoned to say we were safely home, Stefan grabbed the phone and chatted to me at length about what he had been doing, in total gibberish, of course. I'm still Book Granny. I've got a lovely book for him today: it's a miniature pop-up book.

RAFAELLA'S BIRTH

Later this same summer Paul and Vivi's daughter was born and Jackie had a second grandchild.

I spoke to Vivi on the Saturday morning a week before the baby was due. She told me she hoped to have the baby on the twenty-second because there wasn't a World Cup match to interfere with Paul's fun. When I spoke to her, she said, 'I'm glad you've rung because I think I'm getting contractions.' England were playing that night, so Paul wasn't any too pleased. The rest of the day we heard nothing and Frank said, 'I wonder if we ought to ring?' and I said, 'Oh no, if she were going into hospital, Paul would tell us.' As usual, 'know-all' me! So the day passed, and we watched the football match and then we got ready for bed and Frank said, 'Don't you think we ought to take the phone in with us?' and I said, 'No, of course not, she can't be in hospital or Paul would have told us.'

At nine o'clock the next morning the phone rang and an excited, ecstatic, tearful voice said, 'Your granddaughter has been born!' I said, 'When?' and Paul said, 'An hour ago.' 'When did she go into hospital?' 'At four o'clock yesterday afternoon.' I said, 'Why didn't you tell us?' and he said, 'There wasn't any point in telling you anything until there was something to tell.' So, of course, all of Saturday had passed in having contractions, and Frank and I watching the

World Cup and knowing nothing. There she was, all born and an hour old, and we hadn't known anything, so it was very different from Stefan where we'd lived through it all. It was almost an anti-climax. We were all certain she was going to be a girl. Paul had watched her being born and found it the most moving experience. We decided we couldn't wait till the weekend to see the baby, so we rushed up to London. She was a full-sized baby weighing seven pounds four ounces, unlike Stefan, with masses of black hair. A lovely baby!

When Vivi had been home for a few days, she said to me, 'You know I talked to you about having a routine?' 'Yes,' I said. 'Well, it's impossible!' 'I knew that,' I said, 'but I thought you'd better find out for yourself.' It seems funny that I, as a grandmother, find myself preaching free ideas for the upbringing of children; it used to be grandmothers who preached regular spanking and strict discipline.

My feelings for Rafaella are completely different than for Stefan. That doesn't mean to say they're less. I suppose because she's full term, I'm far less protective. I feel over the moon with this baby, but I don't have the other dimension of protectiveness which I still have for Stefan. I can't bear his parents to say a cross word to him, which is absurd because they need to, he's nearly two now and he can be a little bugger! The other day Joanna was trying to put his shoe on, and he kept moving his foot so she couldn't do up his lace, and in the end she shouted, 'Stefan, for goodness' sake!' and he cried, and I bled inside and immediately rushed and did his other shoe up, and I had to give myself a silent smack and say, 'Stop interfering.'

It's just beginning to dawn on me the wonderful scope that Rafaella, being a girl, offers for dolls and dresses. Wonderful! I'm going to be terribly sexist. I can see I'm going to be giving her little toy irons and stoves and tea sets, and dolls, above all, lovely dolls. I'm buying Stefan a slide for his birthday. He's already got a sandpit in our garden and we've got him a second-hand trike from the next-door neighbour, so that will be there when he comes to stay next week.

I am a very organised person. I never realised this until people began to tell me, and I don't always like hearing it, because one likes to think of oneself as above that sort of thing: 'God, how boring!' I certainly wanted to be a very conventional mother. I didn't want their friends to say, 'Cor, look at her!' I always kept their shoes clean and polished and took their blazers to the cleaners. I was a very good mother in those ways and I prided myself on all that, but I don't need to be a conventional grandmother. (I discovered later that the children's friends thought I was terribly eccentric.)

My life has been hugely enhanced by the feminist movement. I came to life again through that when I was forty: Paul was thirteen, Joanna eleven and Julia was six. I was living my life through Frank and through his achievements. His play was on in the West End and then in New York, and it was all very exciting, but it wasn't my life I was leading, but his. The sad thing is that at a later stage he said, 'But I thought my success would be enough for you,' and I said, 'But it was *your* success; and that's not mine. From 1954 to 1967 I was the children's mother, from 1965 to 1967 I was the wife of a successful playwright. I wanted to be me.

I needed the company of women to become myself; I needed the love of women to become myself. As mothers we are so busy nurturing everybody else that we are not allowed to grow ourselves, we get cut off from our spring, so you have to have a revolution in order to grow. I went to meetings, and gradually gained the confidence to join in and have serious opinions and know what I felt about things. I suddenly discovered that women were a political influence, a social influence, that my best relationships were with women, that my best friendships were with women. Women enlarged me and, because I was with women rather than in mixed groups, I learnt to express myself and think for myself and distance myself from just being Mrs Somebody or somebody's mother and became a person in my own right, and that was because of the feminist friends I made and the feminist meetings I went to. I learnt that women were an entity in themselves and a woman is someone in her own right. It was that that made me grow. The women I met then had discovered what I had yet to discover: that they could lead their own lives and be something other than adjuncts to men.

My mother eventually tuned in to what was happening to me and the day before she died she said, 'Well, I don't know, why can't you have an affair with a man like everybody else?' She was wonderful, but she just didn't want my life to be more difficult than it need be.

And, of course, one day I shall want my grandson and my granddaughter, and any other grandchildren still to come, to know me, the real me. I want them to understand there are a lot of different ways of loving and they are all valid, as long as you're not hurting someone else.

CATO GOES TO THE DROP-IN CENTRE

THIS MORNING, ON the way back from fetching Cato, he and I go to a toy shop called Tiger Tiger and buy a farm. I remember all the excitement of buying toys for my son Jem, who could always coerce me into spending money. The farmhouse has roses growing up the wall and a red-tiled roof that you can lift off. There is an open-sided barn and a shed with three stalls. I would have liked one with a pond, but Jem isn't here, so my Puritan instinct gets the better of me and I choose the cheapest and a bag full of animals.

When we get home, we unpack the farm and arrange all the cows and horses and calves and pigs in place, including the girl throwing corn from a basket for the hens and ducks. We manage a few animal noises between us. I take Cato out into the gardens and tidy up the geraniums since I plan to bring them indoors soon. The sun is shining and Cato crawls around the garden and I take his shoes off. It is such a beautiful hot September day, and soon it will be winter and too cold for such delights.

Officially he can walk six steps and when he walks it is a big decision. First he balances himself in the standing position, bottom stuck well out, arms outstretched in case of an unexpected fall, then he lurches forward, an enormous smile on his face, one, two, three, four, five, six, and down he sits, clapping his hands and laughing at his own expertise. Most of the time he prefers to crawl.

He plays with the farm while I make him lunch of spaghetti and peas. After lunch I put him in the pushchair and we go out, heading south, through back streets, towards the river. In a little park in Fulham, surrounded by high flats and approached only by footpaths patrolled by tall mongrels with their noses perpetually to the ground on the look-out for fallen chips, is the Drop-In Centre. Here mothers and grandmothers and babyminders come each and every afternoon with their 'under-fives' to sit and chat and smoke a fag and drink a cup of tea, while Lorraine and Carly and Cheryl and Steven and Wayne and Jack and Cato play in the sand or on the train. We sit in the sun, this world of women, talking about how Clifford and Archie and Emma won't go to sleep in the afternoon, and always get a nappy rash after eating tomatoes. How Charlie never learnt to walk, but one day when he was eighteen months old he stood up and ran.

I am happy here watching the children and chatting the while till Ashley, a great four-year-old drives her trike straight over Cato's foot and then backs off for a second go. 'Ashley, please don't run over his foot, he's only just learning to walk. If I go and have a cup of tea, will you take care of him for me?' Soon Cato, small hand in Ashley's, is being led about and fussed over by the transformed and motherly Ashley. After a while Ashley, like most women, is bored of her responsibilities and wanders off, and Cato is happy playing with a teddy till Steven runs up and grabs it from him and and he cries. 'Steven', shouts Steven's mum, very very loud, 'give the little boy back his teddy!' Steven gives it to the howling Cato. 'Now say you're sorry.' Steven does and I find another teddy for him, and for the rest of the afternoon he is my friend, bringing me little toys for Cato and asking me my name. And I think how lovely looking after children is in the company of other people and how boring by yourself, till Carly bangs my head hard in the door of the mini-ature telephone kiosk while I am on my hands and knees trying to persuade her to let Cato have a turn. In spite of my black, bruised cheek, I like it here, it's 'where it's at'. We don't like being cooped up indoors, we two, and I worry about the electric plugs. We have to be out and about, where it's all happening at the Drop-In Centre.

Now, we go indoors, into the bright, light, circular play-room. A birthday cake with three lighted candles is brought in: it's Lorraine's birthday and everyone sings and shares the cake. The Centre is given a grant by the Council, but other-wise they raise money themselves. 'We've got a cake sale on Saturday'.

After two hours I want to go home and I lift Cato up and carry him towards the pushchair. He starts to cry and I thought of my friend, Louise, and what she would have done. 'Come and say "Goodbye" to Cheryl and Victoria and Ellen, and then we are going home'. I carried him around saying 'Goodbye', and he got into the swing and waved his hand enthusiastically, and then I said, 'Now we are going home', this time he let me strap him in without protest. I must remember who is in charge, *me*, and then do things with style, including him and not just suddenly rush off! He fell asleep as I pushed him through the September afternoon sunshine.

When I have Cato on my own I am completely responsible for him and I feel much closer to him. When his parents are there I want to talk to them and tell them my news, and he wants to talk to them too, so sometimes we are rivals, and I retreat into the background and make tea and become a skivvy in the kitchen.

There is a sadness attached to being a grandmother. Is it because you are no longer in the very centre of life? There is a casting-off of power, you are not so absolutely essential as you were when you were a mother with young children.

It is a shedding of responsibility, a movement towards death. Yet there is also a lightness, a freedom, and the sheer delight of having a child in your life again. I think of a grandmother, not in this book, saying to me, 'I would like to be guardian to my grandchildren if anything ever happened to their parents. I sometimes wonder if I would be allowed to keep them, although I would fully understand if they wanted younger guardians. I have known them so well now that I feel I could continue and be loyal to what their parents would have liked. To me they are a continuation of my family. They fit, they belong. I feel so happy with those children'.

CHAPTER 10

Louise

LOUISE IS A painter and a dancer, who has lived and worked in England and America. Now she lives in a small town in Somerset. She was married to Gregory and they have five children and three grandchildren, although she is not yet fifty.

THOUGHTS AND MEMORIES OF LOUISE

Me, lying on my stomach, bent over the bank of the Kennet and Avon Canal, Louise, holding my feet so I don't fall in, and Ivy and May barking in excitement. Ivy, unable to contain herself, jumps in the water and swims about covered in duckweed. It is a hot day in summer. I am trying to pick a bullrush which Louise wants to paint. Later I pick a little cluster of red and yellow berries from a wayfaring tree. 'Ask them first', she says, laughing, and I do.

It was Louise who, fifteen years ago, introduced me to steam baths. She was at that time living apart from Gregory in the East End of London in a house with no bath and little heating, and we went together to Stepney Green Baths. How warm we were in those rundown baths, eating pickled herring with an old Jewish lady we had made friends with. Once we took a bottle of wine and shared it around, gossiping and steaming to our hearts' content. The baths are gone now, of course and we're both grandmothers.

Louise is not afraid of having no money. If all else fails she manages on next to nothing. I must set some store by status and having money must mean part of status to me: I'm both frightened of being looked down on and frightened of going without. Louise gets lovely clothes in second-hand shops, and eats delicious vegetables and salads from her garden; she's a wonderful cook. She has a terraced house which she shares with her youngest son. It has a little garden in the front with an apple tree, and a bigger garden at the back with no fences between it and the other gardens. At the end is a low wall and then a drop on to the scooped-out bowl of a common. She climbs the wall and walks across the grass to the nearest shop which sells everything.

I can talk to her about almost everything. Perhaps that was one of my most special discoveries about doing this book. By the time you become a grandmother you've had a few knocks, and so it's time to just get on with it. This is a luxury, and with Louise I could talk about my meanness and jealousies and greed and guilt as if we were discussing the local bus routes.

My grandchildren

I never knew my grandmothers, but I have three grandchildren. Sophie is my eldest daughter; she has Lily who is three. My next child is Jacob who has two step-children and a son called Barnaby who is two and a half. Next comes Flora. Then there are the twins, George and Catherine. Catherine has William who will be two next week.

My first grandchild was Lily. I went up to London when Sophie was in labour. She was in hospital and she had a painful and difficult time. When I got there she was pretty tired and I didn't see Lily being born. They let her out of hospital two days later which, because she had had such a difficult birth, I thought was much too soon. I cleaned the whole place right the way through before she came back and made it look beautiful.

I stayed ten days and I treated that time as though she were in hospital. The best recuperation I ever had was after the twins were born, because I was moved out of hospital into a rest home. You could see the sea from my window. I stayed there for ten days and they had a vegetable garden and all the soups were made from things in the garden. At night they'd take the babies away and if they woke up they'd feed them on boiled water, they wouldn't give them milk, and so right from the start they learnt that if they woke up they wouldn't be getting milk, they'd get liquid not milk. So when I went home with the twins their last feed was at 10.30 and they slept through till the morning, both of them. Two babies, it was pretty amazing! It made me sure that that was the thing to do, because they very quickly learnt it wasn't worth waking up for the boiled water.

When Sophie came home with the baby I wouldn't let her do anything except feed Lily, and I kept the house clean and made her lovely food. I wanted to give her ten days of peace, and by the end of it she was looking very strong and well and I don't think she's looked back at all. When she first got home she said to me, and she's the only one that has, 'Mum, where shall I put the baby to sleep?' And I said, 'Well, Sophie, it's up to you, you've got to decide.' And she said 'What did you do, Mum?' And I said, 'After having five of you I think it really is better if you don't have the baby in the same room as you at night. I always put all of you in another room and that way I got a better night's sleep, which was the important thing. I could still hear you if you were screaming, but I didn't hear every snuffle.' Anyway Sophie put Lily to sleep in a different room, and right from the start Lily's last feed was at ten o'clock at night and she slept right through till seven in the morning, and Sophie's always been grateful for that. She often mentions it and says, 'I'm glad I asked for your advice because I have wonderful nights; Lily never bothers me.' And Lily is quite a little madam. She has a strong personality, but Sophie has had a nice time with her, she has really enjoyed her a lot.

I have a nice time with Lily when I go to London, going out and walking in the market and looking at the stalls and talking to people. I don't see her as much as I'd like to because of the distance, but if I did I think we would be very close indeed. Mind you, Lily quite often phones me for a chat, and she's coming to stay with me for five days quite soon.

My son Jacob lives with an older woman who has two children by a previous marriage and they now have a beautiful child called Barnaby. There has been a lot of heartbreak for me in my relationship with this family. For various reasons we can't get on, so I feel it is better not to give even my side of the story until there has been a change. I don't want to make the situation worse. I was unhappy and trying to sort out my own life at the time of their marriage. My daughter-in-law's mother is dead and I think it was hoped that I would take her place at the wedding; this I failed to do. The hardest thing for me over this relationship has been to bow out and let go, because I am someone who always wants to make things better immediately. All I can do is, when I think of them, send them my love and hope that their life goes well: 'for words are but vibrated breath not fine enough to chart the soul . . . and yet too fine and telling all the secret anchor of the soul is cut . . .'

And then Catherine had William. Catherine's very special to me: she's a friend on many different levels, she's a soul friend. I think she's one of the best friends I have. She's seen me through some very rough times and has never made me fell strange or unwanted. She rings me up and says, 'Hello, Mum. How are you? What are you doing today?' The night before last she rang and said, 'Mum, I've got a day off, Dad's taking William out. Come into Bath and we'll go out for a drink together.' I had the most wonderful evening. We met some of her friends and we had lovely conversations. When William was born I was very touched that Catherine wanted me to be there. She said, 'I definitely want you to be there, Mum.'

It was a fairly easy birth. I've seen three other births and it was the most perfect birth I've ever seen. Catherine's body was so beautiful. I've sometimes thought the actual birth is quite brutal with your legs spread apart and bulging, but when Catherine was giving birth, her vulva looked like the centre of a lotus flower opening and William's head came out and was lifted on to her stomach and she crossed her arms over him and cried. Her face – I'll never forget Catherine's face when she was giving birth. It was beautiful, really beautiful!

After that the nurse said to me, 'Would you like to bath your daughter?' I was flabbergasted. They put Catherine in a wheelchair, and I wheeled her along to the bathroom and put her in the bath and washed her, and she was just like a child, her shoulders were quite limp. She was sitting there bemused, and I just poured the water over her and washed her, and then wrapped her up in towels and put her back in the chair and took her back. I'll never forget that. She stayed in hospital for three or four days, then she came home and I went to stay and kept the place tidy and cooked meals for about ten days.

Catherine has been more lenient with William than Sophie with Lily. He's allowed to eat wherever he wants, so he trails around eating things and bits get dropped. When I was feeding children I used to make them sit in a high chair. I wouldn't let them go around with cartons of yoghurt spilling all over the place . . . know what I mean? [Lots of laughter] Catherine's of a different mind. I never said anything, I never said a word. But when I looked after him I wouldn't let him do it. For a while it was tricky for me, because I didn't know whether I could just be myself with William or not, and then I decided I was going to be. Even when he's in his house and Catherine's there, I won't let him do the things that irritate me and Catherine puts on a mysterious face when I'm doing this, almost as if she's not there and can't hear what's happening. She gives little smiles; but William knows what I'm like. When he comes here to stay with me, the first thing he does is pick up the shells that are on the windowsill, and he holds them in his hand and looks at me, and I say, 'No, William,' because what he likes to do is throw them all round the room. There's usually a little period of defiance before we iron everything out and then we enjoy ourselves.

I don't have a regular day. Catherine usually asks me if she wants me to have him. We were talking about that yesterday; she said, 'I won't get put off by your saying "No"; I'll just ask you again and one day I'll get lucky.' The longest I've had him was three days and I was really exhausted by the time he left. He's constantly on the go, into drawers, he's into everything all the time. What I try to do is involve him in what I'm doing. If I'm cooking, I put a chair over there so he can stand up and watch me, and I let him help. He always does the washing-up; he stands up on a chair to do it. The place gets absolutely soaked, but he has a wonderful time for twenty minutes or so. It's also teaching him, because I have to keep saying, 'Gently, gently,' with the glasses and china, so he's learning things because he tends to be quite rough – he scatters and breaks things – but that's just the way he is, and I'm trying to teach him to be gentle. With Lisa, the dog, who is old, I've explained to him that she broke her leg, and now he is quite gentle and touches her carefully, while before he'd go up to dogs and pull their fur.

He's seen me being very angry; I've smacked him quite hard too. Mind you Catherine wasn't here, but I told her afterwards. There was a box of screws on the table that I'd left there by mistake. He emptied them all out on the table and I said, 'Well, that's fair enough,' and let him play with them for a little while. Then I said, 'Now we're going to put them back, William.' 'No!' 'Yes, William, we're going to put them back in the box. I don't see why I should put them back, you took them out and you can put them back.' 'No!' I said, 'You're going to, William, you're not going away.' And I took hold of his arm and said, 'You're not going away till you've put them in the box.' He started screaming and I held him by the hand. Then with his other hand he just swiped them all over the room and at that point I smacked him. He howled very, very loud, but I paid no attention, I just held him there. He only howled for about half a minute and then when he'd finished howling he picked up the screws and put them back in the box, and after that we had a lovely time for the rest of the weekend.

It's much easier for me to have him when Catherine isn't around. He loves water and last time he was here we spent about an hour in the bath. He played and I sat in the bath with him. We have the most wonderful conversations; I love having a conversation with William when nobody else is about. On that occasion, we talked quite a lot about tits. It's ghastly when Catherine arrives to fetch him, because he always starts playing up. He's been absolutely lovely and he's been outside digging in the mud or playing with stones or doing whatever we do and we have had a wonderful time, but when she gets here he's a little so-and-so.

I feel children are the most amazingly strong creatures and they are going to go and go and go. They are going to test you and go as far as they possibly can and, unless you give them some sort of walls around them where they know they cannot go any further, they will just keep demanding and whining and wanting all these things. That's my view and other people have different ways of bringing up their children. It was only because I had five that I had to have rules like that, I had to have time for myself. I used to make my own children go to bed at 7.30, and I didn't mind what they did in their own rooms. They could read books or draw or talk to each other, just so long as they weren't demanding from me after that time.

I think I'm very lucky because, although I have to be strict with him because that's my nature and that's the way I like the house to be, I have a very special time too: I go out with him for walks, and we look at things and climb trees and watch birds, and we're just like two equals on these walks. We point out things to each other – I love that.

A SUMMER VISIT

About three weeks ago Catherine phoned me and told me that she had something to tell me. She said, 'Nick and I are back together.' Nick is William's father and I was thrilled. 'Would you mind having William for the weekend?' I said 'Of course I'll have him!' although I was quite busy at the time. I had William to give them time on their own. I had a very nice time with him, exhausting but good. On the last day I was on the point of phoning Catherine to say I'd have him for another day, and then I began to get very tired and he began to get very naughty. I'd start to do something and he would undo it, so it was two steps forward and one back, and he was watching me to see if I was watching him and he was in a mood to bate me. He wasn't interested in having a nice time, he just wanted to be naughty. I didn't suggest having him for an extra day, so Catherine and Nick came out to collect him and when they arrived he was ghastly. He was absolutely ghastly, he was horrible. He jumped all over them and said, 'I want sweets, I want sweets!'

We had been out in the garden about three quarters of an hour with this going on, and it was a horrible situation, it was really awful. At that point I felt that I was in charge: I was angry with William because he was behaving so badly, and I wasn't going to put up with this behaviour from this child, so I just lifted him up – he was screaming – and took him inside. I carried him upstairs and sat him on the floor, and I said, 'William, just don't do that. Don't jump all over somebody and pull their hair.' He stopped crying and looked me straight in the eye. He went back downstairs and outside and started playing with his paddling pool. But it is tiring, you have to watch him all the time.

I phoned Catherine a couple of days after William had gone home and said, 'How's William?' She said, 'Mum, I've bought him some reins and I've strapped him to his push-chair so he can't give me any grief.' When she goes shopping he gets into the windows and pulls the mannequins down.

Then Lily came down to give her parents a rest. She was really quite a madam. William is a generous person, and they were both in the paddling pool and he had the hose, so I said to William, 'Let Lily have the hose now, William,' and he said, 'No!' I repeated, 'Let Lily have the hose, William,' so he gave it to her, and a great smile came over Lily's face. She had it for a while and then I said to Lily, 'Now it's William's turn,' but, no, she would not give it back. When she had it William stood and enjoyed watching her playing with it, but when William had it Lily was scowling at him.

She has beautiful eyes and she sings a lot and she's hard to resist, but when she's cross she can look quite fierce. She's a typical only child with an enormous imagination, and she plays on her own and likes all her toys to herself.

When Sophie, her mum, arrived she was giving her a hard time saying, 'I want this, I want that,' and I didn't interfere between them, I just let it happen. Then Sophie said to me, 'Mum, tell her,' so I told her, 'Look, for goodness sake, Lily, give Sophie a break, it's her holiday too!' And she just looked at me. I thought, 'I've got two children here, I've got Lily and I've got Sophie, and Lily is being a nuisance to my Sophie!' My loyalty was to Sophie because I don't like tyrants and Lily was being a tyrant.

I feel so lucky that Catherine and Sophie both trust me with their children. I would never tell them how they should bring them up, but when they come here they have to abide by my rules. I have a lot of child in me. I want to cry a lot and I don't dare. When a meal is over I don't want to wash up, I want to run around and play. I want to skip and play hopscotch, but I don't dare tell anyone. I just believe that you should have a nice time in life.

I love my grandchildren in the same way as I love my children. Perhaps this was because I never loved my children as my children; I used to think of them as people who had come to visit me. I used to have a sense of wonder all the time. I have this with William.

I was looking after William because Catherine had gone to the Glastonbury Festival, and about the third day she'd phoned and said, 'I'm fine, Mum, and I'm coming back when the festival finishes.' Well, the festival finished and no Catherine; she didn't phone me and I was worried, I was extremely worried. It was on the second day that we went to Clay Hill. William is wonderful at having adventures. We took a picnic and I had some painting things with me and we climbed up Clay Hill. I found a place about halfway up to sit down, and I said to William, 'You wander about and do what you like.' I knew that I could see him for quite a long distance. Suddenly he asked, 'Where's God Louise?' I didn't say much and then he said, 'Come on, we're going to find God. Come on Louise.' 'Oh William, do we have to?' 'Yes!' I had to get up and he said, 'Come on, we're going to the top of the hill.' At the top of Clay Hill there is a sort of bowl, and he stood in the middle and stretched up his arms and shouted, 'God, where are you? Where are you, God?' When William started shouting, 'Where are you God?' I started shouting, 'Where are you Catherine?' I needed to tell somebody about my worry, so I said to William, 'Look William, Catherine has gone to Glastonbury and she hasn't phoned me and she's very naughty. I'm worried about her.' And he said, 'You smack her, Louise!' I said, 'Yes, I think I will, William.' That's why he's good company, because you can talk to him like that.

Eventually Catherine rang and I told her how worried I'd been, and she said, 'Mum, why ever did you worry? You should have known I was all right.' I said, 'Why didn't you telephone, Catherine?' She said 'Well, I'll tell you the truth, Mum, it was so wonderful to have some freedom from William and to have four or five days with my friends doing exactly what I wanted to do, that I was frightened that if I telephoned you you would ask me to come back and get him.' Now I value that more than anything, that she can tell me that. So I said, 'Another time just phone me and tell me what you've told me so I don't need to worry, and no matter what I'm doing I'll look after him to give you that time.'

There are bleak moments. Each time I have him to stay there are about two good days and one ghastly day. When he arrives I suggest a few things that we might do and he gets very excited. He gets me moving. I do like it as they get older and you can talk to them as people. William is three and a half now. When my own children were little I was too busy to know what really went on. There were five of them in six years, and I was ironing and cooking and cleaning and making their clothes. I didn't really play with them, whereas I do play with William. I was extremely happy being a mother. I was lucky, I loved all the things I did. The only thing I didn't like was the quarrelling. I don't have the strength or the patience that I had in those days. My patience does run out quite quickly now. I was meditating the other day and William was disturbing me and I said, 'William, don't! Just read your book and keep quiet,' and he respected that.

I treat the grandchildren as equals as much as I can. They're not equals, because they're not big enough to stand up and do the ironing, but if we're going to have a picnic then we've got to get the picnic together and we've got to wash up the breakfast before we go, and I make William do all those things. It takes a long time and it's messy, but I just want him to know what's involved in living. I don't want it to be a separate thing, you're the child and I'm the grand-mother. As much as possible I want us to be equals and that's how I was with my children. I always wanted 'my time' and my children were always in bed about seven or half past seven, and I try and do the same with William.

THAT AUTUMN

William erupts into the house like a little colt. He is three years old. He has long fair hair down his back and his mother has cut it short around his face. He has bright brown eyes and a raucous laugh. 'Hello, Louise! Can we go to the woods?' 'Yes, we'll go to the woods, but first I'm going to tell Nell the story of how you got lost on the sand dunes and if you are very, very, very quiet you can listen.' She gathers him up in her arms and kisses him. 'I'm going in the garden, Louise.' 'All right, William, but if you come in and sit on my knee and be very, very quiet, and then we'll get the picnic ready. But you mustn't interrupt because Nell and I want to have fun talking.' By now William has disappeared out of the door. 'Don't run away, William, don't go out of the gate.'

It happened when he was about two and a half. Catherine, William and I took a little chalet in the sand dunes in Cornwall. It was March so there were no other holiday-makers about. On the day we arrived, Catherine said, 'I'll go shopping and leave you here with William.' We make a shopping list and Catherine goes off, and William is absol-utely delighted with all the sand and goes outside and starts digging away. I'm unpacking and then I look out of the window and he's gone. I run to the door and I can see him running up between the chalets. It is very cold and there is a wind blowing and I think, 'I'll just run in and get my sweater on and go after him,' and by the time I come out he has totally disappeared.

I went running round and round the chalets and I couldn't find him. There must have been about fifty chalets, and what was difficult was as I ran round one he could have been going round another one so you couldn't know you had covered the area properly. There was no one about, the place seemed completely deserted, and although I circled each chalet he could have just been out of sight when I came in view of another one. He wouldn't have stopped even if he had heard me calling him, because he just has in his mind this one thing he wants to do and he doesn't care what is happening around him. So I ran around and around the chalets. I felt so frantic that I was beginning to pray, 'Oh

God, if you bring William back, I won't do this and I won't do that . . .'

Nell: I want to hear what you wouldn't do.

Louise: I'm not telling you, Nell. Eventually I decided to find the people who owned the chalet park. They were redecorating the chalets so there were five or six of them sitting in the office having tea, and I ran in and said, 'I've lost my grandson, he's disappeared!' I must have looked completely frantic. They all ran out and said, 'Which way did he go?' 'He went that way and then I lost sight of him.'

Three men went up on to the sand dunes: they were five miles long, just endless, and really high, and two other people went down to the chalets on the beach. I went up on to the road and thought, 'He could have been picked up by a car, and I went running down the road. It's amazing how fast you can run when your adrenaline is pumping (even when you're a grandmother), and my heart was going and I ran a long way, but I couldn't see him. When I came back they were making signals to me and I thought they meant they had found him, but I didn't know if he was dead or alive.

I came running down towards them and one of the men said. 'He's all right: we found him playing down the other end in the sand.' He was carrying him and he came towards me with William in his arms, and I was trembling so much I didn't think I could hold him. Of course William couldn't understand the anguish. . . I took him inside and had a good cry, and I said 'William, I've been really worried about you,' and he looked rather sheepish and said, 'Yes, Louise.' An hour later Catherine came back and I told her and had another cry; I was so shocked and drained that I didn't really enjoy the rest of the holiday.

It seems that for many years I've been sorting through what's happened in my life, and I think that that's coming to an end and now I want to get on with other things which might take up a lot of my time, so I might not have as much time for grandchildren. I've brought up five children. When it's your own children it's hard to step aside and see what's going on. The twins, Catherine and George, will be twenty-one next week: it's time to do some thing else, time to live again, if you like. I think I'm only just beginning to make it clear to myself. I don't want just to be a baby-sitter; I want to be Louise who the grandchildren come to see, and it's good to come and see her because she's doing this, that and the other, and we have a good time with her. All three are toddlers now and that's the part I love, that you can have conversations with them. I look forward to them getting older. I think because of the things I've struggled through in my own life, I also need time now to feel free. I don't feel I have to be there for them; if I want to go to Tibet, I'll go. Whatever I want to do, I'm going to do it and I won't feel bad about it.

Nell: I think now that I'm a granny, I have to be patient and loving and decent and calm, and I mustn't lose my temper, or freak out and sit with my head in my hands wishing I was dead. I must be like everybody's idea of the perfect grandmother who's had her fun and must now be a fountain of wisdom. The problem is I don't feel like a trickle of wisdom, let alone a fountain.

Louise: Why can't you be stroppy? You can be a stroppy grandmother and they can say, 'Come on. we're going to visit stroppy Granny today and if you humour her maybe she'll change your nappy.' Grandmothers are people, for goodness' sake! I think you should be a person and not a granny!

Nell: So you don't think I need be on my best behaviour?

Louise: I've broken that now. I've stopped worrying about how they think I'm behaving with William. I think Catherine is relieved. Remember first you're Nell and then you're Granny. All grannies are people; being a granny is just a situation they've got themselves into. I have an idea that I might get over being a grandmother and get ridiculous again. You've got to get to a point when you've been through hell and then you come to a levelling-off point and you can be very light-hearted again. I think you're taking the granny role very seriously, aren't you, Nell? I think we ought to go outside now and play hopscotch with William!

CATO GOES TO THE SWIMMING POOL, BUT DOESN'T SWIM

YESTERDAY MY FRIEND Cherry and I decided to take Cato swimming. Cherry is soon to be a grandmother herself, and is eager for the practice. We sat at a little pool-side table in our costumes, sipping out hot chocolate, feeling like bathing beauties, at the new Fulham Baths. I could tell Cato was apprehensive about the water; he didn't want me to take his clothes off. Cherry plunged in and I sat on the edge, dangling my legs in the warm water, and tried to persuade him that he might like it if only he would give it a try. He looked firmly in the other direction. He was definitely against it, hook, line and sinker.

Cherry got out and wrapped herself in a towel and took Cato on her knee so 'Granny can have a swim.' Cato didn't like this idea at all. His little face disintegrated into a huge, open gob and squeezed-up eyes starting with tears, and he gave a great yell. 'Give him back, Cherry,' I said. She was all for keeping him and wasn't the least alarmed by his tears. Perhaps if it had been my child I would have said, 'Stay with Cherry because I'm going to swim.' One put one's own children through quite a lot just in order to survive. But although he looks like my son he isn't my son and so I took him in my arms and didn't swim. The swimming pool was noisy. He didn't like it. He stood on my lap, his arms around my neck, looking firmly over my shoulder, away from the shrieking children, leaping and splashing in the water. I didn't like it much either.

When we got home and Cherry had gone and Cato had fallen asleep, I felt a bit bleak. I don't know why it came upon me. It's a familiar feeling, to do with aloneness, loving solitude yet abhorring it. I've had it all my life and I know, if I'm patient, it will eventually go away. In the meantime, I feel bleak, the bleakness of: 'This is boring; I've done enough of this, where's our mummy? We've been together all afternoon, playing with the bricks and we've been very good, so now why doesn't Mummy come and make it all happy and nice?' I want Mummy to come and say, 'Tea's ready, darling, and I'll turn the telly on and we can sing some songs.'

It's as if there's a bit of me that goes missing. Unfortunately, it's the strong grown-up side that takes full responsibility for what's going on. In many ways I like being a spectator in life not a participator. When Cato is being 'good', I am full up with my love for him and 'happy as flowers in May' as Joy would say, but when he is all 'frogs and snails and puppydogs' tails', I want to shout, 'Help! Get me out of here, it's no fun!'

When he woke an hour later, I had dozed too and he was all sunshine. I made boiled eggs and bread-and-butter soldiers for us both. It's a lovely evening so we pile into the car with the pushchair and head for Richmond Park. Cato has learnt to say 'May' and when I call her, he imitates me, but he can't say 'Ivy'. May has disappeared and so I whistle and call, 'May, May, May, May!' Suddenly she comes whizzing through the bracken, helter-skelter, her white body flying towards us up the little path through the green bracken. 'Here she comes,' I say, 'good girl, May-May!' 'Goo gir May-May,' echoes Cato and he opens wide his mouth with astonishment at his own cleverness. I laugh with pleasure at his speaking his first phrase and then he laughs too, louder and more raucously, determined to outdo me in the laughter stakes. Ivy wags her tail and jumps up to the pushchair to lick his face.

We meet a grandfather with his little grandson. It is half-term and the little boy is out with Granddad and the old beagle, to climb the trees and chase the squirrels. We talked and he told me that he had vowed to stop work at sixty, come what may, and have time for the grandchildren. This he had done and he was, he said, 'a fit and happy man'; he had put work behind him the day he left after forty-six years with the same firm and never gave it another moment's thought. Life was very good. The child called him to look inside a hollow tree, so I said 'Goodbye' and Cato and I went on to see Ivy swim in her pond.

After spending the day with Cato I am often exhausted, and yet I am also warmed and softened and stopped in my tracks. The headlong race at achievement is totally abandoned, because who can achieve anything with a young child about? Life slows to a ramble and I have conversations that without him I wouldn't have had, and I become aware of other lives that without him I wouldn't have known.

CHAPTER II

Alice

ALICE LIVES WITH her husband Ber in a seventeenth-century cottage on the Kennet and Avon Canal. She grew up in Yorkshire, but spent all her working life in London; when she and Ber retired they came to live in a small village in Wiltshire. The cottage is one of a group of pink-brick, thatched cottages approached down a footpath. The garden is full of shrubs and flowers. A philadelphus and a cotoneaster hang over the fence, there is a snowball tree and an acer with golden leaves and a little bag of nuts tied to a branch for the birds. Alice is interested in flower arrangements so she grows a variety of shrubs with berries.

On the other side of the patch is the vegetable garden which is mainly Ber's domain, with carrots and potatoes and onions and leeks and lettuces growing in neat rows and a pink rose running riot up a telegraph pole. There is also a row of marigolds and tulips for 'picking' and a large fruit cage which Ber is always having to chase birds out of. In the summer the pair of them are rarely indoors.

Alice doesn't have any grandchildren, but Tory, a neighbour's thirteen-year-old daughter, lives a few yards down the path in the next cottage but one.

There was nothing exotic about my grandmother. She was with me all the time. I was born in my grandmother's house because that was where my parents were living. I was only a few months old when they moved into a house of their own and I stayed with my grandmother while they got settled, which frankly I cannot understand. While I was living with my grandmother, my mother had another daughter; by then I was two years old and they didn't want me because they needed to get used to the new baby. By that time I was getting confused, I couldn't understand that my mother was my mother.

My grandmother was the centre of my life. I stayed with her till I was four years old, then it was decided I should go and live with my parents. I can see clearly the walk to my parents' home. I know which shops I passed; I remember the chemist with all the bright glass bottles in the windows. My grandmother held my hand and she carried my high-chair under one arm. I was afraid the whole way. From then on I lived with my parents, but my grandmother remained the centre of my life.

My mother wasn't a bad women, but she was very selfish and she probably didn't want girl children. She wanted a son, but she had three daughters and that added to the feeling of rejection – we all disappointed her. Somehow, stupidly, that feeling of rejection has stayed with me all my life. I'm easily upset by what people say. My mind tells me I'm wrong, but my nerves tell me otherwise. I feel an intruder. I have an instinct to give emotionally, I feel a deep affection for people quite often, but I can't express it, because they might not want it. I loved my grandmother and she sent me away and I think I felt that I had been more naughty than I should have been. It occurs to me that I punish children by sending them home. I never smack children. I say 'You must

go home!' I don't mind if they pull the place to pieces –
Tory likes building houses out of the furniture – but if they
put themselves in danger or if they are intolerably rude, I
don't just mean saucy, I send them home as punishment.

When I was at school I would sometimes decide to go to
my grandmother. There was a room in her house that was
my room and I sometimes stayed there. Once when I was
out walking with her somebody called her Alice – her name
was Alice too – and I didn't like it, I thought it was wrong.
I was jealous, I suppose. I believed I was more important to
my grandmother than her own daughters, although not her
son. I remember when her daughter had a baby, she went
to stay with her as mothers always did in those days and
someone said to me, 'You'll have your nose put out of joint
now she's got a grandson; she'll like him best!' But that
didn't happen. I was still the most important to her. I knew
she loved me.

She died of cancer, and she was ill for a long time and in
pain. I saw her every day, I never missed. I would sit beside
her, high up on the bed, and brush her hair; I think it soothed
her. Quite often I spent the night there and then one day
my father came and said I must go home. I remember knowing my grandmother was very ill and I didn't want to go
home. I knew she was near the end and I didn't want to
leave her.

I went to school the next day, and they came to tell me
my grandmother was dead. I felt I had failed her, I should
have been there. Everybody was there except me, and I do
believe I should been allowed to stay there, after all I was
nearly fifteen. I never saw her at the end and that was painful.
I didn't know what to do or what to say when they came
to tell me. I just thought it was the end of my world too.
But that's not true, because after death people come back to
you, don't they? I can visualise her easily; she's still there. I
don't actually believe in the afterlife, I have no faith, but

she's here for me. When I die that's when my grandmother will die; when I die my grandmother will die; but not before.

TORY, MY YOUNG FRIEND

Tory doesn't think of me as her grandmother and I don't think of her as my granddaughter. In fact I'm old enough to be her great-grandmother. What we are is friends, we sometimes think along the same lines, it's as simple as that. I've always had children about me – friends of the family. In my time off, I've taken them out, I like the opening mind, but I've worked all my life so I've never had them really close. Babies do nothing for me, I don't know how to treat babies, I suppose I lack the maternal instinct.

I was living here when Tory was born. When she was a baby I didn't see very much of her although they lived next door. She was just a toddler when she started coming in. She used to come running round and kick on the door and shout till I let her in. I can't really remember much about Tory when she was first born, but when she started coming into my house she was still very small; she couldn't reach the door handle and I remember she was very triumphant when she did. She's never rung the bell; as soon as she could reach the door handle she just walked in and that's how it should be. Before she started school she would sometimes be round here all day and if we were in the garden she might refuse to go home for lunch. I expected it would end when she started school, but it didn't. It's just gone on.

When she was small I used to take her for walks and play Hunt the Thimble and Hide-and-Seek. She knows every corner of this house except Ber's room. She's not allowed in there, chiefly because if we've got anything to hide we hide it in there. Her mother's occasionally brought Christmas presents round for us to hide. The thing we played most was 'Let's pretend'. Most people think it's silly once you've grown up, but I don't think so. Tory found my clipboard and she liked conducting a meeting: she'd people the table with committee members and she'd sit at the head. Sometimes she'd be the secretary and write the notes, sometimes she'd be the chairman, never a mere committee member! Sometimes she'd play 'Grown-ups', and she'd sit and talk about her children and how naughty they'd been and what they'd done at school and having to take them to the doctor's.

I used to draw with her and show her how to get effects, and I showed her how to mix watercolours on the page. We used to make things together: Christmas-tree decorations with Play-dough; you make the dough and then bake it and paint it. We used to make sweets together and she'd take some home to her mother. I've also taught her how to make bread; sometimes we make it together and sometimes she'll make it at home. I remember the first time I made bread I couldn't reach the table and my grandmother put the bowl on the floor. If I licked my fingers I got my hand slapped.

When I get photographs from my family of other children Tory doesn't like it. She pushes them out of sight behind the clock. She asks me things directly and I've always told her the truth. I've never put her off with 'You're too young'; I've always explained things to her and that's what one does with a friend – you don't put them off, you tell them the truth.

My heart lifts when Tory comes in, but that doesn't mean I'm depressed when she's not there. It doesn't mean I want her all the time. Once her mother said, 'Tory hasn't been to see you – I'll send her in,' and I said, 'No, don't do that, she'll come when she's ready.' I would hate it if she came out of duty. I would rather not have her come at all, because that would break the relationship completely. She owes no duty to me and I owe no duty to her. We just love each other, but don't tell her that because 'love' is a sloppy word. When she comes back from holiday she very quickly comes over here once they've unpacked. And if I'm in here she looks through the window at me, and there's a big grin on her face and of course there's an echoing one on mine. We don't hug each other.

I see her going to school in the morning from my window and I can tell by the way she walks whether she's fed up or she's cheerful. If I hear her I'll peep out of the window just to have a glimpse of her, but I don't stay there because I'd hate her to feel she was being watched. She's not being watched, but if I hear her voice I like to catch sight of her.

Once she was in a mood – I hardly ever see her in a mood – I had gone to her house to give her something she'd lost and she was rude to me, very, very rude and I said, 'Don't talk to me like that, Tory,' and I walked off. Her mother told me later she had said, 'You must go and apologise to Alice,' and Tory said, 'I'm not going to apologise to Alice; we're friends, you don't apologise to friends.' She never did apologise, but she came over and walked round and round the house looking in at the windows, and she could see me sitting down reading a book, and I just went on reading and she went on round and round, and after a while she came in and said, 'Hello,' and I said, 'Hello, Tory,' and we went on from there.

She often gives me gifts: this house is strewn with gifts from Tory, like that little blue pot there. Sometimes she goes to a jumble sale and she thinks 'Alice would like that.' I always get something if she's been on holiday. She made the soft toys on the couch and I've got more upstairs. When she was young she always bought me a Mother's Day card and a bunch of flowers. She's got that sorted out now, but I still get a bunch of flowers. That's very flattering and makes me believe she thinks about me.

I think if you run after a child you lose them. You have

to let a young child come to you. My grandmother was always there; whenever I went she was there. I can't remember going to the house when she wasn't in. She never made demands on me. I could just be with her – something stable.

I have a rule that no child is allowed to go past the apple tree because we are on the edge of the canal. If they go past the apple tree they are sent home. I am very clear about them not doing things that put them in danger. I just make simple rules and I explain them, and it's a very firm 'No'. Apart from these rules I don't mind what they do.

I like having a child in my life because they have a fresher outlook. It gives me pleasure when I hear Tory using a new word, when I see her discovering something new. Once I had bought a pair of new shoes, and she ran home and found an old pair of hers with the same pattern and came back wearing them. She's always interested when I buy something new. She talks to me about clothes rather as you might talk to a sister or a girlfriend: 'Where did you get that?' When I had my hair done, she said, 'Turn round – oh, I like the back, that's nice!' It's not the sort of thing a child says to an old woman, but she's always accepted me, she doesn't think of me as being old. She asked me once if I was old.

Though I have never thought of Tory as anything but a dear child who has enriched my life, perhaps underneath, there is a wish . . . I want to give someone else the stable, loving centre I had from my own grandmother, who I think of every day.

Cato comes to stay for the
weekend

His mother was bringing him over and Dan, the man in my
life, soon to be a grandfather himself, was driving us to the
country at six. She rang to say the car wouldn't start and
she was waiting for a taxi. At last she arrived, Cato was
bundled into his seat in Dan's car, clasping a sandwich, and
we drove off in the pouring rain down the King's Road
heading for Wiltshire and the canal and the woods, May and
Ivy safely stowed at my feet. I wondered what he would do
if it rained all weekend and he missed his parents.

When we got there I carried him down the muddy path
to the cottage. He had slept on the journey and was full of
go, looking this way and that as he recognised the land-
marks. Once inside he wanted to get down and explore, and
I made some scrambled eggs on toast for his supper and then
took him upstairs for a bath. On a stool was a book about
Landseer with a fierce-looking polar bear, teeth barred, on
the cover. Cato patted it and said, 'Teddy'. Dan said, 'Ivy
and May couldn't do that.' Yet looking after dogs does help
when it comes to looking after babies; there is more in
common than you might think. Setting the boundaries, for
instance. I was sure I didn't want Cato to play with my
computer, it mattered too much to me, so I was able to say
'No' with total conviction when he touched it and, after
trying two or three times and whingeing a bit and giving

me some dirty looks, he gave up and got down from my knee and went and did something else while I went on with the computer lesson Dan was giving me. In fact, apart from this half hour of concentration I didn't attempt to do anything other than look after him. Perhaps that is the hardest part: you really can't follow a thought or a conversation through to the end. Everything is fragmented, broken off, stopped and started again.

He was wonderful at going to bed. I'd just start saying 'Teddy! Teddy! Where are you?' – (Looking up the stairs) – 'Are you in bed, Teddy? Then Cato would join in shouting for Teddy too, 'Tedda! Tedda!' (the first word he ever said), and I'd run up the stairs with Cato in my arms, into his room and there would be Teddy in his cot. 'Teddy, *hello!*' And I'd pick Teddy up and begin to kiss him wildly, and Cato would love all this and want to hold Teddy, and then I'd pop them both into bed, kiss them both and run out. It worked like magic. It was cold in the night and I woke; the wind was blowing and I went to see if Cato was covered up. He wasn't, and so I tucked him in and looked out of the window at the apple tree and the stars, then hurried back to bed, hungry for as much sleep as I could get before dawn broke and I heard him calling.

On Saturday the sun shone, and Dan and Cato and I went with Jill and Alan, who live in the next cottage along the canal, for a glorious walk in the Savernake forest. The leaves were beginning to go yellow, the dogs raced among the trees and we all had a go at pushing the pram along the tracks. It was so hot that we found a fallen tree to sit on and sun ourselves, and Jill played Catch with Cato's red hat much to his delight, while we talked about God and going to church and if it was possible to be a good person, which we all decided we weren't, with much merriment.

When I was cutting up the dog's dinner, I made Cato sit on the step and he cried because he wanted to sit on the counter and help me, but I had a sharp knife and didn't want him there. I let him cry and went on with what I was doing, and when I had finished I carried him into the sitting room and sat him down among his toys. When I looked up he was crawling towards me with a smile on his face. He reached my chair and pulled himself upright and lifted his arms. I reached over to take him on my lap, and he pushed his open mouth against mine and held it there in a firm wet embrace, a gigantic kiss.

There were moments of things going wrong. He slipped over in the bath and fell on his back. I caught him before his head went under, and picked him out and held his wet body against me till his sobbing stopped, then I put him back in, but I held his hand till he sat down and I felt sorry that I had, even for one moment, allowed my attention to slip and he had fallen and frightened himself. He didn't seem to think it was my fault and played quite happily in the water afterwards.

We decided to eat with him, so there we were round the table, Cato on the telephone books, his tin plate of poached fillet of plaice, boiled potatoes and courgettes in front of him, and me with the spoon in my hand, blowing on the neatly arranged mouthful to cool it, and suddenly he plunges both hands in the food, scrunches it around the plate and, picking up as much as he can hold in his fists, stuffs it in his mouth, large dollops falling everywhere. He repeatedly pushed away the proffered spoon till Dan said, 'Why not just leave him to get on with it and eat yours?' and this is what I did. Cato has moved on and wants to feed himself. By this time May was hastily eating what had fallen on the floor and Ivy was soon joining in, so I hoped enough went into Cato's mouth to keep him quiet till tea-time. When he had finished I washed his face and hands, and got out the brush and dustpan and the floorcloth. The bib smelt strongly of fish, so I put it in the washing machine, feeling quite delighted with grandmotherhood. There is something almost laughable about finding myself a grandmother, I, who in many ways, feel but a girl myself. It seems such a short time ago that I was buckling the blue leather sandals that I loved so much, all by myself for the first time. I remember so vividly the sensation of bare legs and shorts first thing in the morning. I remember my grandmother saying to my mother when I was about seven, 'She's got pretty legs,' and how proud this made me feel. I remember so vividly being a little girl in a child's body; how come I'm a grandmother now? He is sitting on my knee and my hands are in my lap and he begins to poke his forefinger in my curled fist. Suddenly it all comes back: my father playing this game with me as a little girl and later playing it with my little boys. I realise Cato's father must have taught it to him and passed on the game to yet one more generation. The game is called 'Put your finger in the fox's hole'. This is what happens: you make a fist and the child moves his forefinger in and out of the hole in your fist as you recite the words, 'Put your finger in the fox's hole; the fox has gone to market; when he comes home [your voice becomes menacing at this point], he'll break your bones and put you in his pocket!' On the word 'pocket' you close you fist and attempt to trap his finger. If you succeed (which he half hopes you will), there are wild shrieks of terror and laughter.

I love his loud laughter, his immense pleasure when you share a joke, like him imitating Dan's cough, his hand in front of his mouth, a little discreet clearing of the throat. We laugh and he laughs louder still, a laugh full of glee and gusto. He isn't yet walking along dangerous walls, or getting into moods about not being allowed more sweets, or indeed ever saying he is bored. Instead, when tired, he will come and sit on my knee and lean against me, and last night when I put him to bed, unprompted he blew me a kiss as I left the room.

Perhaps, when he is a young man and I am an eccentric old woman with wild hair and an unsteady gait, I shall be less interesting to him, so why not make hay while the sun shines and pluck the sweetness before my eyes and thank his parents for including me?

CHAPTER 12

Patricia

WHEN PATRICIA LEFT her first husband he took away her tiny children and hid them from her in Brazil. Her second marriage was to a film director and they moved around the world depending on where he was working. Eventually, after many painful years, she re-established contact with her son, Ghigo, and her daughter, Flavia. Flavia is now married to Paulo and they have a son Fernando.

MY GRANDMOTHERS

My paternal grandmother was a very negative person. She was completely polluted by her non conformist religion. Then she became Church of England – they chopped and changed, these old ladies. It was always a cause for argument within the family and with anyone who was around – huge family dramas. It was always those awful bits of religion, so it was tremendously repressive, you weren't allowed to do anything. She didn't like girls and when she saw me with lipstick on, that was the end of it, we never spoke again.

My maternal grandmother was also constantly chopping and changing religion, but she wasn't as repressive and I was fond of her. When I was very little she made me feel special. She was very attached to my mother and she made me feel special as I was my mother's daughter; it went from grandmother to mother to daughter, a special feeling. She lived in India and she was always interested in beautiful exotic places. She went off and lived in Palestine for a while. She brought me exotic presents and taught me to look beyond England for experience. She was a graceful woman and she showed me how to paint in watercolours, but she was so religious they had to be Bible stories, and she'd show me postcards of India or Palestine. To her these places were a lost paradise; she could never quite settle in England. She wasn't a great strength in my life, but she was someone you could have an exploration with. I was encouraged to look beyond the boundaries of daily life. I never felt I was going to have to stay in England.

She used to have a round box like a hat-box and inside were little Bible texts all rolled up like cracker mottos. I lived with her for the first year of the war and when my mother left I was very upset and for a great treat I was allowed to take a text from the box. She lived in a house with oil lamps and she had a collection of Indian brass animals all along the corridor, but at the same time she'd joined a sect called Foursquare Gospellers, and we had to walk five miles there because you weren't allowed to drive on Sundays. I remember it was always raining, and the puddles and the cold. She was always slightly dotty, but finally she became senile, and I found that frightening as a child, being up against the irrational. She also had a deep belief in being ladylike and those two things combined made it virtually impossible to do anything.

I got a barrage of religion from both sides of my family. Part of it was you had to recognise you were basically a bad person. Perhaps the grandmothers had nothing else to do except join religious sects.

When I heard Flavia was pregnant I was very shocked because I didn't hear from her, I heard from Ghigo. I was lying on the floor doing my morning exercises and he said, 'You're a grandmother,' and I didn't appreciate that at all. It wasn't because I didn't want to be a grandmother, but because I wanted to be told by her. I wasn't told she was pregnant; the first news I had was that she had a baby. Ghigo said 'You're a grandmother,' and I said, 'When Flavia tells me I shall know I have a grandchild, and until she tells me I don't know!'

It took a long time before I accepted it. I wanted to know what day he'd been born; until I knew that it wasn't real. In the end she wrote, but it was a bad beginning and I'm only just beginning to realise that I have a grandson. It's very hard for me to say what I feel like, because I wasn't there and I didn't know. It was too many nothings. Fernando is now three and a half and I've just met him for the first time. They came over from Brazil and spent ten days with me in London. What was most important for me about this visit was that I was getting my daughter back. I was aware I wasn't taking a huge amount of notice of Fernando, but he doesn't speak English and my Portuguese wasn't brought back in ten days in a London house – I haven't spoken it for years.

There has been so much separation in my life from Flavia. Her father stole her and Ghigo away from me when Flavia was two and a half and Ghigo was three and a half, and I didn't see them for ten years. Then we were separated again: she was living in Brazil, and Joe and I were living in Paris. She came and stayed sometimes in the holidays and time was made, but it was never only for her. I went to Brazil and visited, but we never lived together.

When she got married and had a child, I think she felt

there was something missing, as indeed I did – there was a gap. So she brought him to see me. We spent the ten days together very simply. We ate our meals in, and did our cooking and our shopping together. I had no help in the house so we just ran a house! It revolved round Fernando and we didn't discuss it, we just did it, and it worked beautifully. Paulo, Flavia's husband, would often take Fernando while Flavia and I were talking, and play with him. This was the most important thing for me. Fernando knew who I was, and I shall grow into him and him into me as times goes on. When Flavia told him I was her mummy, he said, 'No,' but the next day he announced I was his mummy's mummy. I know he's my grandson, but in a way I don't quite believe it: I've only had ten days with him. One evening he came and found me in the kitchen and made a long, long speech to me, and I couldn't understand a word of it. Not only do I not understand Portuguese, but he has a little stammer as well. In the end he got fed up with talking to me.

It isn't an immediate bonding as with your own child, it's quite remote, but I feel very strongly that I wish I had the money for him to go to an English school so he could learn English. I haven't and I feel really sad about that. I'm beginning to get involved with him, but it's taking longer for me than for some people. I believe that family relationships thrive on the everyday and you want to be able to talk about everyday things, like if you got a nice piece of meat from the butchers. You can share those things, but we don't have that. We do have things in common, because we do have things to talk about. I found Flavia so good to keep house with: although we had never kept house together before, everything happened with such speed between the two of us. Like flashes of lightning, things got done. She always fed Fernando, because he had his food whenever he wanted it. We'd eat at fairly set times. It worked wonderfully.

I had imagined I would baby-sit for them when they were staying, but I never did. They'd come such a long way and Fernando was so little and he couldn't make himself understood with me. They didn't want to go out. They felt they had come to be with me and to introduce Fernando and Paulo, and we simply did everything around Fernando so he didn't cry or get angry. If he was hungry he was fed. It was a wise decision they had made. There was a part of me which thought Fernando would be in bed at six o clock at night, remembering the way we lived, but of course he wasn't ever. When he went to bed they went to bed. They couldn't put him on another floor all by himself in a strange house; it would have been awful. I was very impressed by the new parenthood. Not that I would have done that to them as children. I brought them up according to Dr Spock; certainly not putting them to bed at the unearthly hours that we were put to bed, but perhaps more organised. This easiness and the idea that both mother and father were equally involved in looking after him and indeed in taking care of the house – it more than impressed me, it pleased me, it made it all very agreeable, nobody was slaving away. As I look back on it, the memory is that we all did everything together.

I think Flavia is a perfect mother. Actually I thought I was a perfect mother, which in all my circumstances is probably a big laugh. It was very sad that my children were deprived of me, but, yes, I think Flavia is a wonderful mother. It's one of the few areas in which I have total confidence. It's the tolerance, the taking it as it comes. She reacts to each situation as it comes along in terms of letting things develop. I think children are like plants and animals, and you have to feed them, but otherwise – let them grow. It's the ability to sit back and let them grow that is so important and the doing of it which is so beautiful and satisfying. I know I didn't do it. I was deprived of it after the first few years. We only really had the very early times completely together, so our relationship was never whole; as my son put it once, 'You're not like a mother to me, although you are my mother.' I feel my own deprivation was extreme and excessive; nothing will ever make up to me for what I lost. Nothing can ever compensate, this will always be a scar.

Clearly, having had such a disrupted relationship with Flavia, I can hardly expect my relationship with my grandson to be utterly straightforward, it can't be. Not only do we not speak the same language, we haven't met before, we don't live in the same country, not even on the same continent. We'll have to be to each other what we can be, he and I, won't we? But I do see it as something for the future, I've hardly explored it. I liked it that you said you felt remote when you first saw your little grandson when he was just born. This is where I am, he's only just born for me. I don't allow myself to fantasise about having more time with him. It would be the best thing that could happen in my life if we could just live on the same continent. I'm not too ambitious, but if they could just come and live in Europe!

For me grandmothers were these rather cantankerous women with white hair. To society in general they seem to have a nuisance value rather than anything else. I feel in my best moments I've still got a lot of life and work left in me, and I feel like an active member of society and not someone on the brink of retiring. I don't want even to think of that, so I feel I don't fit in to what most people think of grand-mothers. However, I do want to be part of Fernando's experience and background. I'd love to be like my friend Monique: I think part of me doesn't want to be a grand-mother because I'm afraid of getting weepy over something I can't have, because I can't have what she has. Her daughter lives with her husband and two children on the same floor of an apartment block in Paris, and when the parents go out for the evening the children come in and sleep in Monique's bathroom because she doesn't have a spare room. She has two little bunk beds. They come in after supper, and they have some milk or juice, they talk a bit and then they go to bed. She's quite strict, she says, 'Time to go to bed,' and off they go, and I always think, 'How lovely,' because she has an everyday relationship with them. They run in on their way to school to say 'Hello,' and those things I can never have. It's difficult for me to be a grandmother when, till now, I haven't had anything out of it.

I'm like some living example of the terrible separation trauma, am I not? It goes right back to my family. My mother and my uncle were born in India and my uncle was sent to boarding school in England at the age of eight and perhaps that's the interesting point about being a grandmother because I can look back on an uncle who was sent alone across the world at the age of eight, but when my own grandson comes across the world to see me then of course we won't even let him go to bed alone. Things have changed. In many ways the world has improved in the way we treat our children. I remember the hours and hours I spent in bed alone as a child, hours and hours of being alone; all that has changed. Flavia isn't 'the floury-handed' mother, but within her possibilities she's a good mother and I think I'm going to be like that as a grandmother, be who I am, which is not 'floury-handed', but share who I am.

I'm quite prepared to revive my Portuguese, but only if I go there. If he comes here, I want him to speak English. I wasn't there to watch my children grow, like you watch a flower unfolding, to see them emerge, and that's very important. In the spring you look every day and see what's happened to the plants and it's tremendously inspiring. I missed all that. On this visit I was quite conscious that I wasn't making an effort and it didn't worry me. I thought, 'This is my family and you don't make an effort with your family do you? That little boy is my grandson, and he knows it and I know it and there's plenty of time.' What I wanted was to have Flavia here and to talk to her, just to sit together and sit close and to be together, and that was lovely. And we did, we were able to do that.

Now we don't have to go back over difficulties we had when Flavia was growing up and we were still getting to know each other. She came to see me and she brought Fernando. No more explanation is needed. Ever.

CHAPTER 13

Stella

STELLA IS A painter. Her studio is in the garden of the seventeenth-century house she lives in with Richard, her second husband, who is a writer. Her children are all from her first marriage. Stella and I have known each other since childhood. She has three sons, and a stepson and a stepdaughter who are both grown up now. Her own sons are Nicholas, who is thirteen, Anton who is eighteen and Boris who is twenty-two. Boris and his wife Gabrielle have Allegra who is two; they are now separated and Boris has a new girlfriend called Lynn.

MY GRANDMOTHERS

My mother's mother was dead, so that's the end of her, although she was mythically wonderful. My father's mother I remember, although she never came to the house because my parents were divorced. She used to come and see me in her little car when I was at boarding school and I found her very embarrassing. I was appalled when she came one birthday with a Fuller's cake in a box. I was about eight or nine and I was playing games and a girl said, 'Stella, there's a funny little lady who's come to see you,' and I thought, 'Oh God, it's my grandmother.' This nice little old lady was standing there and I didn't even kiss her, and she gave me the cake and drove off again.

Sometimes she took me out for the night. She could never visit me at home, there was no question of it, it wasn't on, but if she took me away from school for a night I rather enjoyed it. I saw there was something nice and special about the way she treated me. She'd make me cocoa which had never, ever happened at home. But I wanted to keep her well away from everybody else. I knew she wasn't right. She wasn't like my mother's friends. There were so many things, like the cups and saucers and the table and how the flowers were: my grandmother would do 'arranged' flowers in a hideous vase, while my mother would just toss wild flowers into a sweet little jug. I knew there was no way she was going to be anywhere near acceptable to those people. I learnt about embarrassment from going to boarding school very young and hearing the judgements made by other children about each other's parents and what type of home people came from. It was very alarming, and she had a Scottish accent too. What a nasty judgemental little thing I must have been.

I remember she wore lovely floral frocks with necklaces and hats, and she said she had a Venus de Milo figure and so did I, and she told me that we had that in common. It meant having a big bosom and little waist. Apparently she was a grocer's daughter in Scotland and she was picked up in the park by my grandfather who was a retired sea captain. She was only twenty and she just managed to have my father before my grandfather got too old. I think she was always struggling to be a lady. She loved her walled garden and she liked making cakes and pastries, and I've taken on both these things. I think she went strange quite early on. She used to go to auctions and bid compulsively for furniture so the house became full of enormous cupboards and chests-of-drawers.

My mother didn't encourage the relationship and it tailed off, which I feel very sad about now. I would have liked to call her 'Granny', but as I didn't even call my mother 'Mummy', 'Granny' would have seemed even more soppy. My mother wouldn't have liked it. My father too was dismissive of her and would say things like, 'Oh she's impossible,' or 'She's mad.' There was, in a way, a very anti-family thing in my childhood. Families were 'silly', sentimental almost.

Nell: As she was your father's mother and your parents were separated, perhaps it was up to him to arrange the visiting?

Stella: I suppose I don't like hearing that because it means that it is up to my son Boris to help me organise my relationship with Allegra. I get rather cross sometimes because Gabrielle doesn't always fall over backwards to help me see Allegra, so when you say that I feel a little caught out, because I agree and then I remember, 'Oh no!'

Nell: I never helped my mother-in-law see her grandchildren once I was separated from their father. I always left it to him. Looking back on it, if I could have written to her and said, 'Thank you for always being kind to me; we are now separated, but please visit if you ever want to see the children' . . . . Perhaps young children need their parent's permission and encouragement to love another grown-up.

Stella: How wonderful it would be if that did work, and you and your grandchild liked each other, but of course it might not be like that and I might be another of these embarrassing grandmothers to Allegra. It's always been my fear, even with my children, that I might embarrass them.

When Boris and Gabrielle had been married a little while they decided they were so much in love it would be romantic to have a baby and they had Allegra. Sadly the marriage hasn't lasted. When Allegra was born I was living in Dulverton and Boris and Gabrielle were living in Exeter about twenty-six miles away. I was very excited about Allegra being born although I was already worried about the marriage. Gabrielle is a silent person and therefore not that easy to get on with, and Boris and I have a warm and rather intense relationship. Boris would tell me something he was excited about when Gabrielle was there and she would say, 'Hey, you haven't told me about that.' I think she was jealous, but all in all we didn't get on too badly. I had a fantasy that maybe Boris and Gabrielle would let me be there when the baby was born. As it got nearer I saw this was a fantasy, but I still wanted to get in on the birth as much as I could. I felt a bit sad that I couldn't be there.

Boris rang to say they were going into hospital. I was thinking about them a lot, a lot, a lot. Then he rang up and said it was a girl and I was a tiny bit disappointed. I would rather have a boy because I know boys. But I was really interested it was a girl: 'Goodness, a girl, now I'm going to have to face knowing girls.' Then we rushed to see her as quickly as possible. Everybody was blissfully happy. Gabrielle was wonderful, more forthcoming than I've ever seen her, talking all about the birth and what it was like. They were both so young, both only nineteen. The other granny, Gabrielle's mother, was already there when we got there and I was immediately jealous of her. She felt I was jealous and started thrusting the baby at me which made me feel worse.

During that first year I saw a lot of them. Boris and Gabrielle came to stay and liked being with us because I would cook and look after Allegra while they went to the pub. I loved being left with Allegra. It was extraordinary when she was little, holding her against me and feeling that babies must somehow give something back, absolute love. I have vivid physical memories of holding her against me, the physical sensation of her body and feeling totally free to love her completely, no complications. With my own children perhaps it was more suffocating, but this felt just a freedom to love.

I still feel nervous in some ways that she's a girl. I'm more frightened of women. I can trust a little boy's love to be more absolute and uncritical. Little girls are so judgemental. Even physically I was rather shocked when she was a baby, seeing her naked, and still now their genitals seem so enormous and they have a big dome of flesh, rather sleek and closed. It was, I felt, almost threatening. I couldn't believe that she was the same as me, or that I had ever been the same as her; it set me trying to remember what it was like being without pubic hair. That is also what moved me and made me love her, having had that rather startled feeling about her, and yet her pureness and vulnerability. She looked like Boris when she was born. I do now see she is like Gabrielle, but she is so quickly racing towards just being herself, although she says things in the same way as Gabrielle.

When I heard Boris and Gabrielle were splitting up I was appalled, although I knew they weren't happy together and I suppose on some deep level Boris's happiness came before Allegra's for me. Very soon Boris brought Allegra to stay. That was very moving: seeing Boris looking after her and trying to keep her happy! I began to see Allegra as sad and pathetic, which she wasn't really. I would find myself saying, 'Poor Allegra; how is she, poor little Allegra?' and Boris would say, 'Don't speak about her like that, Mum, she's perfectly all right!' I realised I was going over the top, seeing

[175]

Allegra as the little victim of a split marriage, so I stopped that.

I desperately want to be friends with her mother. I'd hate her to think I was against her, and when problems between us crop up, it is so vital to deal with these things, otherwise I could ruin the relationship. Now you really can't avoid facing these feelings. When we were younger we might have got away with behaving neurotically and jealously; now we can't, they have to be dealt with. What usually happens is that Boris brings Allegra to stay for the weekend. I haven't yet had her on her own. Gabrielle and I haven't yet worked out a way that I can drop round and see Allegra spontaneously when I am in Exeter, but I think we will get this right. I'm sure Gabrielle wants to safeguard her privacy, but once, when she discouraged me from popping in, I was very hurt so I didn't go round or ring up. Then I felt I wasn't seeing Allegra enough. Three weeks had gone by and I felt I'd like to see her once a fortnight. She's so lovely now; she jumps into my arms when I see her!

Last time when I saw her at Boris's, as I was leaving she wanted to come with me. Boris said, 'You can take her, Mum,' but I was tired and it was an hour's drive home, so I said 'No,' which was probably a mistake and Allegra was very disappointed, but she is a very good-natured child. She didn't make a fuss, she just looked despondent, and I said I'd take her next time. Ever since then I've been planning to have her, and I wonder about it and what time of day I should fetch her and would she get bored on the car drive. I feel worried that the first time, all day with me, should work well.

I decided to phone Gabrielle and say I did want to see more of Allegra and she was very nice. I went to visit them in Exeter and again Allegra wanted to come when I left, so I said to Gabrielle, 'Would it be all right if I came and took her out for the day? Maybe I could do something regularly that would help you?' and she said, 'Yes, yes!' Early on I had decided I was going to be a lovely granny because I love her and that's that. Then I thought, but I'm a painter, I can't go bundling off to Exeter once a week and lose a whole day's painting. I'll have her when she's older and she can come and stay, and then I'll see her more. It seems quite a step for her to stay the night.

Nell: The first time Cato came to stay with me by himself I felt very overwhelmed and nervous, but somehow we muddled through, and now I've had him to stay three times and it has got better each time.

Stella: This is very comforting. I thought I was the only granny who felt panicky at the prospect and other grannies took it in their stride.

I worry about Allegra seeing enough of Boris. When Boris came to see us he brought Allegra and Ruby, the daughter of a friend who's had a horrible life. I found this very difficult. I didn't want Ruby to be there, because I thought she's bound to be disturbed and unhappy and it will reflect on Allegra, and I don't want Allegra to have any difficulties, as she has lots already. I felt quite ruthless. It was quite shocking – I simply didn't want anything to do with Ruby. Boris had come with his girlfriend Lynn. He said to me 'You've got to be nice to Ruby,' and if I was going into the garden with Allegra, Boris would say, 'Take Ruby too, Mum,' and I would think, 'Oh God!' I was appalled, because in a way I identified with poor Ruby, the unhappy, left-out little girl. What also shocked me was how much I tried to hide it from Boris and Lynn: dear, sweet, welcoming Granny was absolutely vicious underneath.

I think I was a good mother by trying very hard and passionately loving them. Gabrielle's a good mother in a natural knockabout instinctive way, rather like she's good with animals and a good rider. I see she's got a different way of mothering which really does work, because Allegra is so lovely and so confident. I see how little I know about the different ways people are going to be happy and how to nourish them.

It makes me feel a bit anxious when you talk of being a grown-up and making choices; I'm not sure I want to grow up that much. I'm feeling more misty than you; I'm not quite sure what I want out of the relationship. I feel more doubtful and less confident. I only just know that she likes me. I'm not even sure what Allegra and I would do together. Although I loved my children being there, being with me, I never played with them, it always bored me. I don't know why I said I was a good mother. I think I made them feel loved. But I noticed with Allegra that I'd think, 'This is lovely,' when we'd settled down together on the floor and she was playing with a trumpet. After a few minutes, I thought, 'Oh dear, I'm a bit bored by this.' I don't know what I'm going to do about that. I wonder how profound my ambiguity is? I wonder if it's just being daunted by the technicalities. She's in Exeter, I'm twenty-five miles away. She can talk now, is she going to go back to Gabrielle and say . . . ? Oh it's silly . . . I *have* been cross with Allegra. It was quite thrilling and fully justified. She cried and then she soon stopped and on we went. That gave me great confidence.

Looking back it never occurred to me that my granny was ever going through anything troublesome. By far the biggest difficulty in all this is me and Gabrielle; because of the split-up, our relationship can be strained. If they were together I think I could be more relaxed. I could be more everyday, more knockabout.

Now there is a new difficulty. Lynn, Boris's new girl-friend, is a little jealous of Allegra. I understand this because I've had jealousy over my stepdaughter, and so I was very sympathetic to Lynn. I'd been there myself, so I felt protective towards Allegra. When they came to stay I would look after Allegra so they could go out and Lynn wouldn't feel Boris spent all his time on Allegra. I would love taking care of her and we both enjoyed those times together. Then Lynn, who is a very brave, tough, good woman, decided that the way to overcome her jealousy was to get very involved with Allegra, and she has. She buys her clothes and changes her nappies and has taken over rather. The next time they came to stay, I was longing to take care of Allegra and Lynn would be doing it. The other day Anton was clearing out his room and he found some old toys he didn't want and Lynn said, 'Oh great, I'll have those toys for Allegra.' I said 'That's a good idea; they can be for Allegra.' Allegra's got a toy box in our house and I thought they would go in the toy box, but no, Lynn took them back to her flat, to her toy box, and I thought, 'No, no! Granny's house, full of old toys! They should stay here,' but I didn't dare say so, so the toys went. I think I will be able to talk to Lynn about it, but I'm not absolutely sure. It is a bit comical, but also it's a bit serious because she doesn't feel that established with Allegra herself, while of course if she were the real mother she would be saying, 'Oh yes, do take care of Allegra.' As it is, she's rather wanting . . .

When Lynn arrived the other day Allegra was asleep in her arms, and I longed to take her and carry her upstairs, but I didn't. Because Lynn's not Allegra's mother, I don't think she realises the passion and needs of the grandmother. But it's up to me to tell her, isn't it? And even though I'm jealous sometimes, I'm so pleased Lynn loves Allegra too. All this will get sorted out in time, if we're brave.

Stella: I've forgotten to bring a photograph of Allegra. She doesn't look like me – not that I'd want her to, but I'd like to see a link!

Nell: Cato doesn't look like me either.

Stella: Oh, but he does! Cato looks exactly like you.

Nell [Secretly delighted and flattered]: Oh, do you think so?

Stella: Yes, I do. Anyway Allegra's got big blue eyes and a slightly olive skin, a lovely mouth and quite a long upper lip like me. She's got rather a big head like Boris, and fair hair, very long and quite untidy and lots of hairgrips. She loves hairgrips and necklaces and things. She's very thin, which slightly worries me, and a little odd about food, but she's very strong. When Margot brought her daughter to stay, she's a very sturdy little toddler six months older than Allegra, and I noticed Allegra was much better at running up the bumpy stones on the beach and splashing in the puddles – she's very tough! When we got back, the two little girls sat at the table and drew. Ruth was very good at it and Allegra just scribbled, but it was all very nice. Allegra came into my bedroom early next morning and clambered on to my dressing-table stool and surrounded herself in make-up which she loves. I think we feel very comfortable together. I love her coming to stay with Boris, and when Anton and Nicholas are there too. I like us all being at home together.

Last week I took her to a museum by the castle. It has huge stuffed animals and cases of birds which she loves, and you press a knob and there would be bird song. And I would say, 'Look, Allegra, how lovely!' and she would say, 'Oh, how lovely!' She is very interested in animals and birds. I get in a complete dither when I'm out with her: I'm constantly following her. She's two and a half now so she can run quite fast, and I can barely pay for the tickets or do anything other than concentrate on her – what's she doing, is she safe, does she want me to lift her up, is she getting bored? She said a wonderful thing to her mum when she got home; she hadn't eaten any lunch, although I would have liked her to have lunch so we could sit at the table together, and when I told Gabrielle this, Allegra said, 'But I'm not hungry – I'm happy with Stella!'

She did get hurt when we were in the museum cafeteria. She lifted her head too quickly and banged herself on the railing, and she saw I was upset and so she started to cry, and I put down the tray and held up the whole queue while I comforted and kissed her. I could see the cashier lady looking at me as if she thought I was rather over the top.

If I moved away and only saw her about three times a year I don't know what would happen. I know I have to lead my own life and moved away if that is what's happening, although I see I'm getting more involved with her. When I passed the bead shop I saw some lovely hairslides and it gave me a shock of excitement to think I could buy one for Allegra but they looked rather delicate so I didn't. She loves clothes and Gabrielle buys her such wonderful things: she's got a jersey with a pocket knitted as a bus and inside three little knitted people are poppered in. You can unpopper them and pull them out and look at them and then popper them back in. She has purple shoes with coloured laces that she loves. Boris gave her a party frock that he bought in Taunton market. It is peach nylon with a sticking-out petticoat, absolutely beautiful.

Nell: It sounds the sort of dress that I longed for as a child and would never have been allowed.

Stella: Oh no, much too vulgar! It hangs in the sitting room at her house on a hanger so she can look at it. So far she isn't at all spoilt, she never asks for things in shops.

She isn't really like me and I think I'd be unnerved if I saw myself again. When she was a baby I got so involved

[181]

in feeling such a lot of love for her. As she gets older I'd like to show her some of the things I loved as a child: going to artists' studios, their houses, the smell of their paints, the way they were, catching a glimpse of that world. My way of doing things might contribute to her choices, to her way of doing things. I like showing her my paintings. What I want to be for her is an unjudgemental, all-accepting grandmother who she can turn to when she's twenty and in a terrible muddle and everything is against her, and she comes and stays with me and is completely relaxed and unbothered, and she can just feel she is wonderful in my eyes. Although not too wonderful, so she has to live up to expectations – that would be the ultimate! Of course if she painted, I would love that, I would be fascinated, but if instead she was a good rider I would be very happy. I have none of the expectations for her I had for my own children. I don't really mind what she does; I'd just like her to be in my life.

CHAPTER 14

Rebecca

REBECCA'S CHILDREN ARE *Nick, Clarissa, Judith and Christopher. Nick is married to Steph and they have four children: Jonathan, Lionel, Poppy and Sophia. Clarissa and Joe live together, and they have James and another child on the way. When I first saw Rebecca she was wearing a red romper suit and she was in her mid-fifties. We were at a dream group, and I described a dream I had had about being on a train with my sons, and they got off at the station and I was left on the train with all the luggage. I think it was to do with learning to ask for help.*

I used to feel some constraint when Rebecca and I were together and I finally understood what it was. She was such a good mother, she had made such strong adult ties with her children, she already had a grandchild. She had achieved so much I wanted that I felt inadequate when I was with her. Finally I told her how I felt. Her blue eyes opened wide and her mouth dropped open, showing her lovely white teeth, and she began to laugh, and so we became great buddies. She was the one who started me off on the idea that it was thrilling to be a grandmother.

MY GRANDMOTHERS

Both my real grandmothers had died before I was born. My father's mother died of TB when he was eleven. My mother's mother was killed by a taxi in Belgrave Square when she was a young woman. My mother told me she had been a very fierce person and she had strapped her into a tight liberty bodice as soon as she began to grow breasts so they didn't show. She was a repressive woman who thought sex was a nightmare. She married my grandfather who was twenty-five years older than her and knew nothing about sex till the wedding night. My mother told me about it. My mother was very free. In fact she was a raver!

My father's father had married again and it was this woman, my father's stepmother, who I knew as Granny, and she was a lovely woman. She was a good granny, specially to me, and I loved her. She was very religious and took a keen interest in my religious upbringing and made sure that I was confirmed and sent me Bible readings, but she also took me to the theatre when I came to London and that was special for me, very special. I think her gentle presence in my life was of tremendous importance to me, but I think I'm a different kind of grandmother. I'm more like my mother. I like to cook cakes and pies, and play in the trees and go down to the stream and do those physical things with them. My step-grandmother was a more remote person. I would never have got into her bed like my grandchildren get into mine. She lived in London and had 'staff' and led a very protected life. She tried to teach me how to be a lady and say 'coat and skirt' rather than 'suit'. She was shocked that my mother had run away and left her children. She thought my stepmother was very common. She bought me clothes and I always loved the dresses she chose for me. She encouraged me to talk and complain about things I didn't like. She didn't expect me to be a good little girl who kept her mouth shut. I knew she loved me.

My first thought about being a grandmother before I knew I was going to be one was that I wasn't ready for it. I'd just finished bringing up four children by myself and I thought, being a grandmother is going to be the same thing all over again. When Nick and Steph said they were pregnant, I thought, 'What am I going to do? I'm going to have to make an effort and I'm just beginning to enjoy my freedom and my single life.'

I saw Jonathan the day he was born. Nick rang me early in the morning and I went whizzing along to the hospital, and there was this little tiny quiet person, already a person, lying beside Steph. She was looking incredibly relaxed as if she'd done it all her life, and Nick was tremendously proud of the way she had given birth. I felt so excited: here was Nick, who had always said he never wanted to have children, with his first child and completely overjoyed. I immediately knew I must be a support and a help. The hard work of having children and bringing them up was so fresh to me that I knew what they were embarking on, and I wanted to do all the practical things that would help them cope with the grind. The first thing I started doing was cooking things so that when Steph came home from hospital the fridge was full. Those were the sort of things that were very clear to me that grandmothers did. My own mother, who had nothing to do with my upbringing because she had left my father when I was tiny, was a very good grandmother. She was my model. She used to come up from the country every week with a huge steak-and-kidney pie which she had made the night before. And that would last us for two or three days. She was a hopeless mother, but a good grandmother.

Steph and Nick weren't married when Jonathan was born and they didn't intend to get married. Later they changed their minds and when Jonathan was seven months old they had a wedding. I felt so distressed and desolate at losing Nick, I was shocked at my feelings. I really knew that this was the end of my place at the centre of his life. I hadn't recognised that when Jonathan was born; I was so excited about this new person in the family, and so completely trusted that I would always have easy access to this child and that they would want me to be part of his life, that none of those feelings came in till they got married. Then I didn't feel Queen Bee any more, although it wasn't until the day after the wedding that I woke up in floods of tears and cried for two days, I was so desolate about it.

I felt really angry with Jonathan because Steph had asked me if I would hold him at the wedding and I was very honoured to be asked. What happened was that he started screaming in the registry office and I decided I should take him out of this solemn procedure. He was screaming and yelling and the registrar was looking disapproving, so I went out and paced up and down outside while they got married and I wasn't there. I was devastated; in fact it makes me want to cry when I remember it. [She cries] I still have such regret about it; I was so upset and I really felt very angry with Jonathan and angry with Steph for asking me to hold him when that was likely to happen, and I felt angry with myself for being flattered enough to agree when the most important thing for me was to be there when Nick got married, and I wasn't. I think that was partly why I cried so much afterwards; I couldn't believe that I hadn't witnessed it.

When I think of it now, I don't think I really had a relationship with the baby when he was new. I felt I had a close relationship with Nick and Steph, and I was part of a team, and the baby was just a little person who would get by without me, so I was supporting them and I wasn't concerned about making a relationship with him. I liked gazing at him and thinking how beautiful he was, but I was more involved with talking to Steph about what it was like and how the breastfeeding was going. I was still working then, but I'd dash down in my lunch hour, almost reliving my first baby with her, listening to how many poohs he'd done and how many hours he'd slept.

I remember feeling a sadness about the passing of time, a nostalgia, because I so loved having little children, and I felt sad that those days were over, and it did feel like a chance to relive some of those experiences and feelings. In the early days I saw myself as their ally. I didn't really see myself as a grandmother because of not making a particular relationship with Jonathan. And I don't think that relationship began until he started to react and respond, and then I loved singing nursery rhymes to him. I found I could stop him crying by singing to him and holding him and dancing. I loved dancing with him in a rhythmical way [Lots of giggles as Rebecca shows me], then we began to play Peep-a-Boo and I loved making him laugh, I loved that giggle.

Over the next six years Nick and Steph had three more children: Lionel, Poppy and Sophia. Now that they're older the relationship seems much stronger, and my sense of the solidity of it comes from knowing that they know me: not just me knowing them, but them knowing me. They know how I'm going to react and Poppy, the little three-year-old will say as soon as she arrives, 'You're going to love it now because we're here,' because I say to her, 'I always love it when you're here.' So I feel they know me. Nick told Poppy that I was coming and she said, 'Oh well, then there will be big hugs and kisses.' They'll save up things to tell me that they know I'll be excited about.

It took me longer to get a relationship with Poppy, my third grandchild. I think that was because by then Jonathan and Lionel were coming over to spend the day with me on their own so our relationship was getting stronger as our contact was more prolonged. On a typical Sunday, when they were coming to spend the day with me, they would arrive very early in the morning because I love an early start. They started coming for the day when they were about eighteen months old, first Jonathan and then Lionel. Nick would drop them off at about eight or half past, then we'd sit about catching up on what had happened to us since we last saw each other. Lionel would say, 'I've got some more news for you.' Directly they got here they wanted a biscuit or something nice to eat, then we'd go down to the shops and we always had to buy sweets, and then we'd take Jessie, my dog, on the heath.

I used to take Jonathan and Lionel out in a double push-chair and they loved me to push them very fast, and once we were going down to the shops with this double buggy and they kept saying, 'Faster, faster,' and I got completely carried away and ran so fast that it swerved and hit the kerb and one of the wheels came off, and Lionel said, 'Daddy will be very cross.' I always got lunch ready the day before, because they were so wanting my attention that I couldn't do the lunch and have them here, but they were wonderful at drawing and listening to tapes. They never asked for the telly because they haven't got one at home. They had their favourite songs and nursery rhymes. Lionel has always been very quick with buttons and he's been able to operate my tape machine since he was about two. He'd shout to me, 'Quickly, Granny Becky, it's Nellie the Elephant!'

I found changing nappies really difficult. I could never get the pin in those beastly terry-towelling nappies that Steph used. When they're wet you can't get the pin out and when they're dry you can't get the pin in! She was wonderful, though, because she always used to arrange the nappies in the shape she wanted me to put them on, and put them in a carrier bag for Nick to bring over, so I never had to arrange them.

Getting them ready to go home was the most exhausting bit, because they always brought a case with their things in and we would have to sort out which were their things and which were mine, and find their shoes. The first thing they do when they get here is take their shoes off and run about barefoot.

I think that Steph is a natural mother and Nick a natural father. I think that they're wonderful parents and I see them as needing the balance of the two of them. Steph is very permissive and Nick is quite strict, and I see the children kicking against Nick's strictness, but being contained by it.

If I don't like something I can't help saying it, and there have been days when they've been here when they've really made me very cross by either fighting or nagging me. I remember one day when I was taking them home, we were walking down to the car and Lionel said, 'I think I'm going to call you Cross Granny and I think I'm going to call your house Cross House!' I felt very chastened and I said 'Oh Lionel, have I really been very cross today?' and he said 'Yes.' And I said 'Well, you do do things that make me cross and then I seem to get crosser and crosser.' It comes quite easily to me to say things like 'Don't shout at me, I'm not deaf!'

I think sometimes I haven't been very nice and in that way it doesn't feel any different than I was with my own children. I never feel on my best behaviour with them. It's a terrific handful having three of them for the day. It's hard work and very tiring. They all talk at once, they all want my attention at once, and when I'm talking to one, another is shouting, 'Look at me.' They don't talk among themselves very much, they talk to me. There are times when they've been here for the day and I've said, 'Now we're going to have a quiet time and you're not allowed to talk to me.' I've had to do that for my own sanity sometimes. That's the most tiring thing, the talking – talk, talk, talk, talk, talk! They never, ever, shut up and they're very noisy, they have extremely loud voices. None of them has a quiet voice. I suppose they have to shout to be heard because they're all at it at once.

They do things that upset one another and that makes me cross. I'll see Jonathan push Poppy off the deckchair so he can get on to it, then I'll shout out of the window, 'I saw that!' like a policewoman. 'Say sorry!' Jonathan looks sheepish. I'm terribly bossy. They're very good in the car: they're used to it. They sit in the back as good as gold, and on the way home, they're as tired as I am and they all fall asleep.

✄

CLARISSA HAS A BABY

I got so excited about Clarissa being pregnant, much more than with Nick and Steph. There's something special about mothers and daughters. I've always felt very close to Clarissa and Judith in a different way from the boys; we're women together and we understand each other and we know the things that will give each other pleasure in the way that women know. It's such fun – like going shopping together before the baby was born. I found myself feeling really proud of my pregnant daughter as we walked around John Lewis at Brent Cross to choose a pram. 'She's my daughter and here she is about to have a baby.' We asked a woman with a tiny baby which were the best first-size vests: it felt like a real excursion together, I was included. Again it was a bit nostalgic getting the clothes ready for the first baby: there's nothing quite like it because for the second one you've already got the clothes. It's a sort of nest-building which I loved being part of with her. She'd show me the baby's room and how she planned a shelf here and something else

[190]

there: I felt included in all the preparation bit, it was as if we had a lot more to share.

The whole birth was much more engaging, Clarissa being my daughter. I started getting really anxious about the birth in a way that I never did with Steph. I started thinking that Clarissa's first birth was going to be like my first birth – a complete nightmare – and how could I protect her, what could I say to warn her without frightening her? All those kinds of things that I never had with Steph. I was popping in to see her most days, because she had stopped work and doesn't live very far away. I felt very anxious and uptight just before and then, by chance, I was with her when labour started. We had a hilarious time because Joe came home and he had a stopwatch, and he wanted to go out and do something and he wanted me to time the contractions, and I couldn't work the stopwatch and there was poor Clarissa having a contraction and laughing at the same time. 'Hey, it's me you're meant to be looking after!'

Eventually Joe came back and I went home, and I felt so tuned in to what she was going through, but I wouldn't have wanted to be there. She went to hospital in the small hours of the morning. I slept a bit, but not a lot, and as soon as dawn began to appear I thought, 'Why hasn't anyone rung, what's happening?' I was getting very anxious thinking something must be wrong. I started getting frantic and about six o'clock in the morning I rang the hospital. I knew I wasn't meant to, but I did and said that I was Clarissa's mother, and the nurse who answered said 'The baby's born, but don't let on that you know because if the father hasn't rung you yet I want him to give you the news.' I heaved a sigh of relief, but then I thought 'Why hasn't Joe rung? Something must be wrong.' The next two hours were absolute torment.

He didn't ring till about eight o'clock – he was in such a state himself, he was in pieces. He found the whole thing a nightmare. He couldn't bear seeing Clarissa in pain. He didn't tell me that at the time, he just rang and said 'We've got a baby boy,' and he sounded completely wiped out. I went rushing along to see them and they both looked complete wrecks. He said after the birth he hadn't wanted to leave Clarissa and that they'd stayed together in the labour ward and he didn't want to go to the telephone; he'd never expected it to be such a shattering experience. They were very shocked because James had to be pulled out by forceps and had huge bruises on his face, and they thought he might be scarred for life. They were terribly upset. Of course the bruises went in a few days.

It didn't occur to me to go to the hospital till I'd heard from Joe. I felt it was their time to be alone together with their baby. That night of waiting was excruciating, but I didn't feel that I had a right to be there unless they wanted me. The painful bit was not knowing.

There's a wonderful feeling between Clarissa and me now she's got James, of us both knowing what it's all about. It's lovely for me that she wants me to be a close grandmother. She makes it very clear to me that she wants James to have as much contact with me as he can, and it's a great joy to me that she wants that. I've been on holiday with them and I go there every week around bath-time and put him to bed, and then perhaps baby-sit while they go out.

When she first came home with James, she was in a lot of pain from cracked nipples and very frightened taking care of this tiny fragile thing, making sure he was still breathing. It was just at that time that Judith's back got bad and I felt very torn. I wanted to give Clarissa more that I was able to to because of Judith. I remember going to fetch Judith – she was coming to stay with me because of her bad back – and stopping by Clarissa's on the way home, and Clarissa was in bed crying because she was so sore and wondering if she was doing it right, and Joe passed the new baby to Judith to hold, and Judith could hardly hold herself up and she backed off, and Joe looked upset, and I felt completely torn with these two daughters in such pain. And what to do? It was awful, I hate remembering it. I was so excited about Clarissa having the baby, and I felt at the time I wasn't able to be there enough. We came back here and Judith took up residence. It was a very hard six months for both of them.

One afternoon when James was only about two weeks old, Clarissa decided to walk over with him in the sling to have tea with me and Judith. She was about half way there when she realised she couldn't go any further. She rang up from a call box and I heard a strangled voice saying, 'I'm stuck in the Holloway Road; please come and get me!' I said, 'Wait in the foyer of the Odeon Cinema,' and I hopped into the car. She was in such a state when I found her, in tears and exhausted, and I thought, 'God, what it is being a grand-mother!'

CLARISSA HAS ANOTHER BABY

It was different from James's birth because Clarissa and I had talked a lot about everything so I was more in touch with what was going on. I was also part of the scheme of things to look after James during the birth of the new baby, so Clarissa and I were in touch constantly during the last few days. She'd ring up in the morning and I'd ring up in the evening to see if anything had happened. She timed the birth brilliantly: I'd taken two weeks off work and she started labour when she expected to, so I went nipping over with my suitcase which was all ready.

I got there after James had gone to bed. Clarissa and Joe went off to hospital together about nine o'clock and then I'd gone to bed and, lo and behold, Joe returned and said that labour had slowed down so he'd come home. He settled down on the sofa downstairs and I was in their bed upstairs and James was fast asleep, and at about five o'clock the telephone rang right beside me. I picked it up and it was also beside Joe, who also picked it up, and it was the hospital to say labour had started in earnest. Joe promptly went back to sleep again.

I couldn't possibly go back to sleep and so I got into my 'I mustn't interfere' mode and the minutes ticked by, and after about three-quarters of an hour I went down and put the kettle on rather noisily, and I was boiling with rage. I was thinking, 'How can he, oh my darling daughter, why aren't you rushing there?' He emerged when he heard this rattling in the kitchen, and I said 'Joe, what's happened?' and he said, 'I went to sleep again.' 'How could you?' 'They said it wasn't urgent.' I said, 'But Clarissa needs you . . . and it may speed up, it's her second baby! How can you be so laid back?' He then got the wind up, rushed back into the sitting room, put on his clothes, tore out of the door without a cup of tea, ran all the way to Highbury tube and that was the last I saw of him. He rang when he got to the hospital and said, 'I just thought you'd like to know I got here and everything is going along fine!'

Later Clarissa told me he had arrived in a terrible sweat. What was sweet was that he took time out during the day to ring me and let me know how things were going. James and I got up and we both came over to my house for the day. Joe rang at lunch-time to say things had been pretty grim, but now Clarissa had had an epidural and was much more comfortable and they expected the baby to be born at tea-time. Luckily I was busy looking after James and I tried not to get too fussed. Joe rang back again quickly and said 'We've got a little daughter!' She had almost had to have forceps, but she asked to try three more pushes and the baby was out. I was absolutely thrilled and wondered whether to tell James or not. I thought, 'Would it be very interfering of me? Should I let Joe do it?' Then Judith rang from a call-box and I said, 'Joe's just rung and it's a girl.' Judith said, 'I'm in Oxford Street and I'll go there immediately. Can I talk to James?' I put James on the line and she said, 'So you've got a little sister!' So he heard from Judith, and she rushed straight there and saw them even before they were out of the labour ward! Look, I've got a photograph of Judith holding Ella who is still wearing her little cotton hat.

James is getting used to Ella. He took the odd clout at her when she was new and said, 'Enough bosom,' but he's settled down now and she has her bath with him and it's going well. He is nearly two and he comes to me once a week for the afternoon. It's different there being just one of him rather than the gang of Nick and Steph's children. You don't have to tell him not to fight and only to talk one at a time. James loves playing on his own. I just open the toy drawer and he gets stuck in, or he rolls on the floor with Jessie the dog. He potters out in the garden – I've got a paddling pool and it's been such a fantastic summer.

If he goes upstairs and is silent for rather a long time, I suspect he's in the face cream so I go up and have a look. He'll open any drawer and have a good look, but he knows about not wrecking things. He amuses himself more than Nick and Steph's children used to when they came here. It's a combination of his personality and the way his parents have encouraged him to be. Steph hasn't encouraged her children to play on their own; she has to be interacting with them all the time and she does. All the time she's talking to them and they're talking to her and even when they're talking to one another, she will interject, and so they come to expect that.

James has a little mat for the table, and when he comes he insists that I put it on the table in his place. Then he pulls it towards him so that it begins to slide off, and things get nearer and nearer to the edge of the table and he waits for me to react, and I say, 'Don't do that! You're doing it on purpose and the lunch is going to fall on the floor and I won't like that.' He goes on doing it and I say in a crosser voice, 'I'll take it away or you'll have to get down from the table,' and then sometimes he stops, but not always. He knows very well when I mean it. Even when he doesn't understand the words he knows exactly what I mean. Sometimes he sees how far he can go with Jessie. He pinches her tail and gets very passionate, and clenches his teeth and squeezes her ears, and I'm afraid he's going to hurt her. Jessie doesn't growl; she just tries to shake him off. He's beginning to be quite naughty at times, then sometimes he's angelic for hours on end.

The way I see Clarissa responding to James seems familiar. I feel very at home with the way she talks to him. Sometimes I feel at odds with the way Steph talks to her children. She has to tell them everything in detail and also answers questions for them. I asked Lionel if he knew what angels were and before he could open his mouth Steph answered and I said to her, 'I asked Lionel.' She said 'Oh well, I know what he's going to say.' Clarissa would never do that. If I asked James what angels were, Clarissa would just sit and wait for him to answer and see what he said. It's an enormous difference. Sometimes if one of Steph's children asks me something and Steph isn't happy with the answer I've given them she will expand it, add to it, change it slightly, or say, 'What Granny really means is . . .' If I complain she might clap her hand over her mouth and say, 'Oh, I've done it again!'

Once when we rented a house for a holiday together, I put one room aside as a playroom and said to the children,

'Now, grown-ups are not allowed in here unless you invite us.' Steph was always in there! I find telling Steph about something to do with the children harder than I do with Clarissa. Steph is a natural mother, but Clarissa's mothering is inevitably closer to my own. If I thought Clarissa was doing something back to front, I would say, 'I'm sure it would work better if you did it this way; anyway give it a swing.' I wouldn't have any difficulty in doing that with her. She has involved me in things she was having difficulty with and said, 'How do you think we should tackle this?' We did a great joint project together last summer on holiday, extricating her from a habit she had got into with James, that she couldn't leave the room till he had gone to sleep because he screamed. It was very difficult to break, but we worked it out together and it only took us two nights. This was the campaign: we put him to bed and then left the room and he yelled. Every five minutes we went in and cuddled him and tucked him up. It went on for forty minutes the first night, and we spaced out the visits more the second night, and the third night he didn't do it at all.

Lately I've been helping Clarissa put James and Ella to bed if Joe isn't there; it's very difficult with two tiny ones. If I can get James down without any difficulty I'm so proud and then Clarissa says, 'You are brilliant, Mum, he never goes down so well for me!' It's only fifteen minutes' drive to their house, so it's very easy to pop down at bath-time to give her a hand and read James a story and then nip home.

Sometimes Steph has asked me what I think about this or that and I've told her. I think she plays far to much with every new baby and I think that's hard on the others, she's baby crazy. I've often said that Jonathan, the eldest, doesn't get enough attention, and he can be very difficult and cause disruptions. I'm interested to hear that they've now started letting him stay up a little later so he has some time on his own with them, because bang, bang, bang, the new babies kept arriving. There was one occasion when I told them I'd talked to my spiritualist about him, and I told Nick and Steph, 'Betty says Jonathan shouldn't wear red and shouldn't be given red toys.' Well, they took absolutely no notice and usually when I see Jonathan he's wearing red! [Lots of laughter] I feel they put red on on purpose because I'm coming, just to show me how crazy I am!

Being a grandmother isn't like having children all over again, that isn't what's happening at all. It's being in close touch with children, which you probably won't be if you don't have grandchildren. You stay aware of children, the way they think and the way they play, and the way they boss one another about, and the things that worry and delight them. You stay really in touch with all those things that, once your children have grown up you don't have. I enjoyed it all so much when my children were young, and before I had grandchildren I used to watch my neighbours' children coming home from school and really envy them that coming together after school and hearing what had happened. Although I don't have that daily contact that I see going on up and down on both sides of my house, I certainly have weekly contact on the telephone with Nick's children and I have contact several times a week with Clarissa's children at the moment, mainly because Clarissa's at home and it's a lovely chance to see more of her and she'll be working again in January. I think my grandchildren bring that fresh childlike attitude into my life and keep it there, and I relish that.

Yesterday when we were talking about living alone, I realised I so seldom feel that I live alone because I have so much contact with my family that I can't imagine feeling lonely. If I did, I would ring somebody up and talk to them, but I have so much contact with my children and feel so nourished by this contact. Through having children I learnt that I was a lovable person and perhaps I do assume my grandchildren will love me. Mind you, when my children were going through adolescence I was a perfect pain as far as they were concerned and even in their early adult lives. Even now they love me and they judge me whereas tiny children don't.

I do depend a lot on my children, but I don't know how much I need to worry about that. They are absolutely central to my life, my children and my grandchildren, and I also know that my life has to be central to me too and that I mustn't limit myself by using my loving family as bondage. 'I mustn't do this or that because of the children,' – that's where I think it gets distorted. For instance, if one of the children is going through a difficult time about one thing or another, I get very anxious on his or her behalf and try to work out ways in which I could help them financially. 'If I raised a mortgage on my house I might be able to do this or that,' or when Judith was here with her bad back, I'd think, 'I won't ask so-and-so in, because Judith will be on the floor of the sitting room and it will be awkward or tiring for her.' But finally I know I must be a full person in my own right in order to be able to nourish them, so I don't feel anxious about the fact that they are so central, but I know I have to guard against bending my life to accommodate them in ways they're not even asking me to do and writing the script for them and imagining their expectations. If I do that then I know I've got it out of balance. Apart from that I know what a lucky woman I am.

A WALK IN RICHMOND PARK

IT IS A CHILLY day in Richmond Park. The sun and the moon are out at the same time and little patches of frost glitter here and there. I walk fast to warm up, pushing the pushchair over roots and bumps, Cato bouncing up and down. We watch as an old stag walks solemnly up the hill and I shout at the dogs not to chase him. A calvalcade of horses canters past. We make our way to the little farmhouse and I balance Cato on my shoulders so he can peep over the paling fence and see the bright-eyed brown pony looking over his stable door.

So, am I pleased that I'm a grandmother? In a way, I'm furious − I want to be twenty again. I don't like all this growing old, and yet being a grandmother is one way of staying 'in the thick of it.' Being in close touch with a child, I learn about the new generation. Life is so interesting 'in the thick of it' even when you're a grandmother.

We go on to 'Secret Bench', not so secret now it is winter and the bracken has gone brown and folded over towards the earth. I lift him out of his chair on to the short turf. He can walk now and he potters about, dropping sticks down a rabbit-hole and trying to fit bits of bark back on a fallen tree. I can see May and Ivy seriously investigating under a distant thorn-tree. I sit on the grass and build a miniature wigwam with sticks. Cato plonks down beside me to look and adds more sticks and leaves till it collapses. He has his lovely mother's green-grey eyes and yet he is so like his father, who I remember pushing in his pram down the Fulham Road in a heat wave, bare-legged and bare-footed, eating an ice-cream cone. Were the pavements really that clean, or was I such a show-off then?

I remember the adventures we used to go on, his father and I, on buses around London. He was but a year or two old and I a slip of a young woman. It wasn't Richmond Park that attracted me then, but grotty Chinese cafés in the East End and abandoned railway sidings. He took it in his stride, falling asleep on the way home on the bus, face and hands and clothes grimy with city dirt and yes, that is the quality they have in common, he and his son, a way of exploring the world, of looking carefully at everything. When his father was three, he said to me, 'We live in a magic world.' Cato reminds me that this is true.

Now Cato wants me to crawl under the tree trunk with him, he doesn't quite dare by himself, but I'm too fat to make it, and eventually with lots of encouragement he wriggles under all alone and emerges on the other side full of smiles and sits down to clap. I retreat back to the bench and Ivy jumps on my lap. Cato toddles over and I lift him up beside me. The birds are quarrelling in the trees and below we can see geese flying over the glimmering ponds. Winter is here, it will soon be Christmas.

I didn't expect this child to be such a source of affection. He doesn't 'give his grandmother a kiss' or even two kisses. Instead his kisses are a rainforest where the rain never stops falling, little soft kisses on whichever bit of my face is nearest at that moment till I say, 'Cato no more,' and I am almost hysterical with laughter and pleasure. He too, resting between kisses, laughs, and for me there is the pure delight my grandmother must have felt when her great-grandsons tried to pull her out of the stream and she fell backwards convulsed with girlish giggles.

Now May jumps up beside us and, seeing there is no room on my knee, gingerly perches herself, half on, half off, Cato's rather inadequate lap. Wild with excitement he pats her heartily. May jumps down and disappears into a rabbit-hole. Cato clambers down after her to investigate. He stumbles in his new shoes and rolls over on his back and cries. I pick him up, hug him and put him in the pushchair. I've lost his mittens and his hands feel freezing. He holds them up to me, grumbling. I blow on his small pink fingers to warm them up and then pull his sleeves down over them. Time to go home. So on we go, along the bumpy path, trudge, trudge, Granny, Cato, Ivy, May.